ARE NON DIVORCEABLE
A WORKBOOK FOR DIVORCED PARENTS AND THEIR CHILDREN

AGES 12-18

SARA BONKOWSKI, Ph.D.

ACTA Publications
Chicago, Illinois

To my sisters
Virginia Sue Edgell (Hood) and Susan Elizabeth Edgell

two wonderful sisters, whose vitality and fun-loving ways
are always with me.

Acknowledgments

This book reflects the struggles of many parents and their adolescent children. I want to acknowledge their openness in allowing me to know them and be a part of their family during a time of pain and rebuilding. It is because of them that this book was possible.

As always I have received help and support from my family during the writing of the manuscript. My son, Brian Bonkowski, did much of the proofreading, and my step-daughter, Kim Mulherin, patiently listened to my ideas and gave me feedback from the perspective of a high school senior. During the writing, my daughter, Karla Bonkowski, bombarded us with "news from college," which reminded me that there is life beyond high school. My husband, John Mulherin, as always, provided the stable supportive environment for my writing.

My typist Sarah Grail was energetic in her work on the manuscript. She accommodated my needs, making the writing process easier.

Finally, I want to acknowledge Mary Buckley and Greg Pierce of ACTA Publications. Mary and Greg have a vision of providing help and support to families under stress. It is this vision that provided them with a commitment to allow this book to be written. In addition to being a great administrator, Greg Pierce is an editor par excellence!

TEENS ARE NONDIVORCEABLE
A Workbook for Divorced Parents
and Their Children
Ages 12-18

BY SARA BONKOWSKI, Ph.D.

Dr. Bonkowski is Associate Professor of Social Work at Aurora University in Aurora, Illinois, and the founder of the Myrtle Burks Center for Clinical Social Work in Glen Ellyn, Illinois.

Edited by Gregory F. Augustine Pierce
Design by Hirt and Associates
Typesetting by LINK Book Development
Artwork by Isz

Copyright © 1990: ACTA Publications
4848 N. Clark Street
Chicago, Illinois 60640
(312) 271-1030

Library of Congress Catalogue No. 90-062137
ISBN 0-915388-36-7
Printed in the United States of America

C O N T E N T S

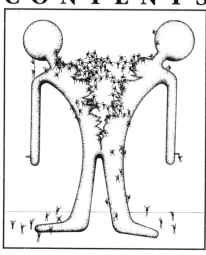

CHAPTER 1

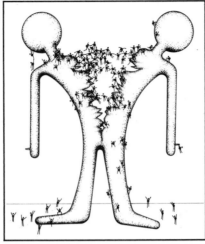

BEGINNING TO REBUILD

"I feel like I don't even have a family."

Matt, a sixteen-year-old

All children—including those in their teens—are in some way affected by the divorce of their parents. Even those children who show no observable signs of stress due to their parents' divorce are sure to react in some way at some time. On the other hand, *not all* problems of children of divorced parents are divorce-related. Children—especially adolescent children—in families with two parents living together also have many difficulties. Identifying which issues in each child's development might be connected to the divorce and then dealing with those issues in a sensitive and mature manner is the special task of every divorced parent.

Matt's mother and father, Diane and Jim, separated about two years ago. Matt and his fourteen-year-old brother Craig assumed right along that their parents would reconcile. After all, they reasoned, it was only a separation and on weekends their dad seemed to be spending a lot of time at the family home. "I don't think my parents will really get divorced," Matt confided to a counselor.

It was a terrible shock to Matt when their mother told her sons she had a court date for the divorce. He felt sick: If his parents were going to abandon him like this, upon whom could he ever count? It felt like his dependable world was slipping out from under him—just when he felt he needed some stability in his confused world.

During their separation, Matt's parents had made a real effort to help their boys adjust to the upcoming divorce. Both parents and children attended counseling, discussing the changes in the family. Jim remained involved in Matt's and Craig's busy lives. He coached their football team and often came over to help with homework. Diane had remained in the family home with the boys—thus keeping their routine much the same. Neither Jim nor Diane were dating or planning remarriage, so the boys were not faced with the parental loyalty pulls that often accompany divorce.

Despite all his parents' careful preparations, however, Matt felt terribly saddened when their divorce became a reality. He became morose and depressed and began to act out in school—even to the point of threatening to drop out. His brother Craig, on the other hand, reacted with casual acceptance, even relief, that the tense situation between his parents had been resolved. Craig's only overt concern was whether he would still be able to continue going to professional basketball games with his father.

The opposite reactions of these two brothers illustrates the variability of adolescent responses to parental divorce. Surprised by both of their sons' reactions, the parents realized they would need to continue their efforts in helping Matt and Craig during this critical time of transition.

ADOLESCENCE

No matter how many signs there or how much warning was given, no child is totally prepared for the divorce of his or her parents. There are, however, great differences in how children in different stages of their development understand and accept what has happened to their family. Recognizing developmental stages and offering suggestions to help young people from infancy to young adulthood is difficult enough—without adding the special situations caused by divorce. For this reason, the focus of this workbook has been narrowed to children between the ages of twelve and eighteen—what we call "adolescence" or "the teens." (A companion volume to this book, *Kids Are Nondivorceable*, is available for parents with pre-adolescent children ages six to eleven.)

Teenagers do not always fit neatly into anybody's categories. Adolescence is a time when humans witness many painful and sometimes radical changes. Physically, the start of adolescence is marked by the beginning of puberty and changes in the body: growth spurts, hair in new places, fuller hips and breasts, deeper voices. Some children begin these body changes as early as nine or ten, and some as late as sixteen. Yet for most boys and girls puberty begins about eleven or twelve.

Psychologically, the adolescent is pulling away from parents. Pulling away may result in fights, yelling, tears. As quickly as a teen may storm out of a house, he or she may return as cheerful and helpful as a ten-year-old. There is a need for an adolescent to be grown up and a need to be childish. The adolescent usually does not understand the changing moods, and parents often become bewildered and worn out.

Most twelve-year-olds are seventh graders. In many schools junior high is composed of seventh and eighth grades, and the building and learning curriculum is structurally different from the younger grades (sixth grade is sometimes included in the junior high, although this is often the result of balancing enrollments rather than developmental grouping). High school is primarily made up of fourteen- to eighteen-year-olds. This school structure reflects the increasing need of adolescents to be with peers. "How am I in relation to you?" is a question adolescents constantly ask. They ask this question in hopes of deciding once and for all "Who am I?" Am I smart, pretty, dumb, a jock, a poet, a nerd? What is it like to follow the rules/break the rules? Talking incessantly on the phone, often just after leaving friends, is necessary because when you are a teenager the task of learning about yourself is pressing and never-ending.

If adolescence begins with puberty—at about twelve years of age—when does it end? When one graduates from high school? When one marries? When one votes, enters military service, can legally drink, etc.? Pondering the varying societal and legal sanctions that may mark the end of adolescence makes it understandable that many adolescents are never quite sure when they are "grown up." Perhaps adolescence has ended when one has a firm sense of identity and when one has developed the ability to commit to relationships outside the family. Once in a while, this is accomplished by eighteen. Most people do not completely master these tasks, however, until their mid-twenties. After eighteen, many older adolescents move away from home. This next phase of life is referred to by developmental psychologists as the "young adult" period. Children who are in the young adult phase of development are not emotionally immune from the effects of parental divorces. A discussion of their needs is beyond the scope of this book, however. Thus, for this workbook adolescents are defined as youngsters of the ages of twelve to eighteen—junior high and high school-age students.

EARLY AND LATE ADOLESCENCE

Even considering the span from twelve to eighteen is a big task! Adolescence may be divided into two phases: early adolescence (12-14) and late adolescence (15-18). These groupings represent somewhat arbitrary dividing lines, however, and your children may not really fit the division.

7

Younger teenagers are strongly pulled toward peers. They begin to experiment with who they are by changing ways of dressing and talking. The young adolescent very much wants to be like and be liked by his or her peer group. Not being accepted is the biggest fear. The early adolescent may have a boyfriend or girlfriend, but—except in isolated cases—sexual involvement usually does not occur at this young age. These younger teens are still very dependent on parents for money and transportation. Girls in this age group are usually socially and physically more mature than boys of the same age, often seeking a one-on-one steady relationship with a boy. Boys at this age are more likely to hang around in groups, maybe occasionally walking a girl home or calling one on the phone. The early adolescent is practicing for more intimate relationships that will follow.

In late adolescence, the child naturally pulls further away from parents as a preparation for a final departure. This pull is often an emotional distancing, evidenced by not seeming very interested in the family. Parents often say that their child seems "cold" or "uninterested in others." The older teen may drive and often works part time. He or she is developing ways and means of becoming more and more independent of mother and father. Sexual intimacy to one degree or another may occur in dating relationships, and the older teen begins to consider what it would be like to marry. A heavy weight of responsibility for future adult life is felt: "What will I do with my adult life?" "Should I go on to college or get a job . . . and if so what college or job?" These life decisions, made at the same time one is separating from the family, are of such emotional proportions that they may result in depression for some teenagers.

All these adolescent developments occur amid the blare of music, messy rooms, homework, curfews, and friends. This confusion surrounding the adolescent often keeps the psychological and emotional struggle within the teenager hidden from the parents. Parents sometimes think that it must be great fun to be as free and irresponsible as their children. To the adolescent, however, life may be okay, but it sure feels as if there is a lot of pressure involved. When a teenager must also cope with the divorce of his or her parents, that pressure can sometimes seem unbearable.

THE PROCESS OF ADJUSTING

Rebuilding a family after a divorce is not easy or pain-free. Each family member has experienced many losses and now has major adjustments to make. In addition to their personal losses, family members often feel social stigma. Although divorce is no longer an unusual phenomenon, it still often carries negative connotations for those involved. The terms used in divorce— "plaintiff," "defendant," "fees," "alimony," "custody," "visitation rights," "non-custodial parent"—communicate a legalistic, objective system that certainly influences a divorcing family's future. How awful it feels to have these terms applied to oneself!

A family is not just a legal entity, but a unique, very personal structure. In writing about divorce, however, one cannot escape the use of legal terminology. These concepts have been designed by the judicial system and the legislature to protect both the divorcing couple and their children. While it is important to look at legal realities such as visitation and custody issues in a human, caring manner, the fact remains that in divorce there are legal constraints and limits for each parent and the children.

The ideas and suggestions in the following chapters have been gathered from several sources. As a clinical social worker, I see divorcing families—children and parents—in family and individual therapy. I facilitate adjustment groups for divorcing adults. I also lead a Saturday morning group for school age children whose parents are separated or divorced. I have seen some families from the time they first begin to contemplate divorce and other families that came for help only after years of bitter post-divorce hostilities. Many of the case illustrations cited in this book are drawn from these clinical experiences. To preserve anonymity I have, of course, used fictitious names and have altered other identifying information relating to the children and families. Some of my (present and past) clients may think that they recognize their children or family situations, but I assure them that this is only because many factual divorce situations, conflicts, and struggles are remarkably similar.

In addition to my firsthand experience in helping divorcing families, I study, teach college classes, and conduct research on aspects of the family and divorce. Finally, I am a parent, with two children, and I personally experienced divorce almost thirteen years ago. Some of my close friends have divorced, and we have shared with each other—as good friends do—our own reactions to divorce. I have observed my own children's and my friends' children's adjustment to divorce. This book is, therefore, an integration of clinical, scholarly, and personal experience.

Divorce is often such a difficult trauma for all family members that children may feel that they are unable to continue to grow and give after their parents divorce. To help your adolescent child regain a positive life outlook on life, draw upon any source that is helpful—this book should be but one of your resources. Others may include family, friends, professional counselors, and your religious faith or organization.

THE EXERCISES

Teens Are Nondivorceable will highlight adolescent development and explore how parental divorce may hinder the developmental process of teenagers. The purpose of this book is to aid you—as your teenager's primary "helper"—to work with your teenager to keep to a minimum any damaging effects of your divorce. Included at the end of every chapter are suggestions for exercises or activities designed to promote expressions of feelings and generate information, ideas, and experiences that will help both you and your teenager understand and eventually accept the divorce. Reading this book and doing some of the suggested activities will also promote an open, honest relationship with your developing child. Through this process—reading, sharing, doing—you and your children will begin to heal, mend, and rebuild a sense of family.

There are three sets of exercises after most chapters: one for the parent, one for the younger, and one for the older adolescent. There are also suggestions for "table talk" on each topic that can include other members of the family and even relatives and friends.

Most exercises for the parent are to be done a day or two (or even a week) before working with the child. Each parent exercise is very similar in format and was designed to help you work out your ideas, feelings, and possible solutions related to each topic before working with your teenager. You will be more open to listening to a teen after you yourself have faced the feelings and thoughts each topic raises. Thus, when working with your teenagers, you will be better prepared to be a calm, sensitive, somewhat objective helper.

The topics and exercises in this book are arranged in an order that will be most helpful in the rebuilding process of an adolescent:

- helping children understand why their parents divorced
- assessing the changes the divorce created for each child
- understanding how divorce affects the normal aspects of adolescent development
  1. separation from parents
  2. positive sense of identity
  3. expression of appropriate sexuality
- discussing the problems associated with visitations, custody, child support, and other post-decree concerns
- realizing how other significant people play a role in divorce adjustment
- dealing with the difficult issues of parental dating and remarriage
- and finally, projecting the future for each child and understanding how parental divorce continues to be an important influence throughout life

Each topic tends to build on the proceeding one, so do the exercises in order. A teenager may not be emotionally ready to think about the future, for example, when he or she has not yet dealt with the past or present.

HOW TO DO THE EXERCISES

Many of the exercises use some type of "projective" technique such as writing a story or letter. In a projective experience, a person will draw upon feelings and ideas that may not be fully conscious. Putting these ideas and feelings into words can be very healing and therapeutic. Just *doing* the exercises can help children experience and resolve conflicts. Please try not to "over talk" your teenagers, or they may begin to dread doing the exercises. Of course, when a child wants to talk about ideas and feelings the project has stimulated, be ready to listen and share—it will help both the child and you.

Your adolescents' response to the exercises may reveal that they are feeling very sad or very angry. It is often difficult for a parent to hear these powerful feelings, for they do not want their children to be in pain. To help your teens feel better you may be tempted to say, "Oh, it isn't that bad," or, "You really don't hate Mom (or Dad)." Please don't. If you discount your children's feelings or give a message that only happy feelings are acceptable, you will not help them deal with your divorce. Working on the exercises can be one way for your teen to ventilate feelings that might otherwise be suppressed.

All people have a right to their own thoughts, feelings, and ideas. Your teenagers' reactions to your divorce may be somewhat different from yours. Remember yours are not necessarily right and theirs wrong. Each person has his or her own perspective, and your child necessarily has an adolescent's perspective. It is not your task to get your children to "sing the company song," that is, agree perfectly with you. Your children will view the divorce from their individual points of view. You, of course, see the divorce events from your perspective. *Both of you are "right" and neither of you is "wrong."*

Your task in helping your teenagers is to allow them the freedom to express their own feelings and ideas, while being willing and able to give accurate, factual information when they need or want it. This will not always be an easy task, but your love for each child makes it possible.

The abilities and interests of children between the ages of twelve and eighteen will vary considerably. A "young" twelve-year-old, for example, may be very willing to sit at home and play a game with Mom or Dad, while the idea of doing so for an "old" eighteen-year-old might seem ludicrous. Each of the exercises tries to take into consideration an adolescent's age and skill level. Do not, however, hesitate to use an exercise designed for a younger child for an older one, or vice versa. You might also want to adapt a particular exercise to your specific needs, or invent an entirely new exercise on your own.

Proceed with caution! Remember: adolescents are trying to pull away from their parents, so your teenager may not appear to be interested in any of your ideas. On the other hand, some adolescents enjoy doing activities and are very interested in processing the divorce issues. Do not force your children to do the exercises exactly as you have planned, or even to do them at all. Give your teenagers the opportunity to choose a time when dealing with the divorce is possible for them and when engaging in a creative project with you might be fun for them.

If you have more than one child between the ages of twelve and eighteen, some of the exercises will be fun to do with everyone working together, while other exercises are best done alone—allowing each individual some private time and attention. If you do joint exercises, however, be sure that you stress that each child may have different ideas about a particular subject—and that this is all right. The discussion of these different perspectives while working on the project may help enlarge each of your children's view of divorce. (A variation to working with just your own teen might be to allow one of his or her own friends whose parents are divorced to participate in some of the exercises. Hearing a friend express his or her feelings about divorce might free your own child to do the same.)

A special situation can occur in a so-called "blended family." If you have remarried after a divorce and you and your new spouse both have children from previous marriages, you may be faced with the question of involving both sets of children in this process. Only you and your mate can make that decision. On the one hand, it may be important for you to have some private time with your own natural children where they are free to express their feelings away from their new step-family (and for your new spouse to do the same with his or her children). If the relationships in your new family are very good, on the other hand, it may be helpful to do some of the exercises together with everyone.

The exercises use materials most families have at home or are able to obtain easily and inexpensively. Some exercises require no materials, only time to spend with your daughter or son. When planning to do an exercise, be sure to pick a time that feels pressure-free (as much as that is ever possible for a single or remarried parent), and have the recommended supplies on hand.

Despite careful timing and preparation, some teenagers may be resistant to doing the exercises. If a child has this reaction, do not push him or her. The time may not be right to share feelings about the divorce with you. In this case, proceed through the book, doing the exercises with other children or only those designed for the parent. Later on, perhaps in several months, you may once again try to do some of the exercises with that adolescent. Other children might love to do the exercises right from the start and will look forward to your special time together. At times a child may like the exercises and at other times appear resistive. All these are very natural reactions.

If your teenager always declines to do the exercises, understand that this may mean he or she doesn't feel emotionally free to deal with the divorce with you. Perhaps your son or daughter would talk more freely to a friend or relative, a professional counselor outside the family, or—as much as you might hate to admit it—only with your former spouse.

The use of the exercises suggested in this book may stretch out over six to nine months, whereas other parents and children may complete all of the exercises in several weeks. If your teenager resists doing the exercises, try to assess whether he or she is defending against looking at the divorce issues or just prefers doing something else at that particular time. Both are good reasons not to do the exercises, but the two underlying reasons mean very different things. A defense against looking at divorce issues means "Go slowly, do not push"; a desire to do something else at that time means "Try me tomorrow."

WHICH PARENT?

Either parent—mother, father; custodial, non-custodial—or both can bene-fit from reading this book and doing the exercises with his or her teens.

If you have your children with you only twice a month you might want to try an exercise every other visit. The time your children spend with you is special. If you or your teen feels pressured to get through the book, it may destroy the natural flow to healing. The exercise may begin to feel more like work than fun. On the other hand, if one weekend is especially rainy, and you find yourself with nothing to do, perhaps you both will be open to and excited about doing a couple of exercises.

Perhaps you are one of those lucky divorced parents that has an open, non-hostile relationship with the other parent. If this is the case, you may want to tell your former spouse that you are reading this book and doing the exercises with your children. This would give that parent a chance to read and think about the same ideas. I strongly recommend, however, that children *do not* do the exercises at both homes. This puts far too much pressure on them. If your former spouse is working with your teenagers from this book, allow him or her this privilege—at least for the sake of the children! The worst thing for them would be for their parents to fight over who does the exercises with them. There are suggestions in the book about how two parents can cooperate in raising their children after a divorce.

On the other hand, you and your former spouse may have a cool or hostile relationship. If you are in this situation, do not suggest the book to your former spouse. This does not mean "Keep it a secret from Dad (or Mom)." It means allow your former spouse the freedom to adjust to the divorce in his or her own way. Your suggestions regarding the children, although designed to help them, may be viewed as an intrusion or interpreted as an order. Do not use this book as another weapon in the marriage wars, but rather as an aid in healing and rebuilding both yourself and especially your teenage children.

A WORD OF CAUTION

Medicine, which can be very helpful and life saving, often also carries with it warnings about its misuse. In such a vein, there are some important concerns that must be raised before you begin.

When discussing some of his or her divorce-related concerns, your adolescent may express some very private thoughts, feelings, and ideas. These must *never* be shared without the child's consent unless it is directly related to the child's survival.

Likewise, the exercises you do with your children must *never* be used against your former spouse—*especially* not as ammunition in conflicting legal issues such as custody, child support, or visitation. What the children share with you in an open, trusting moment must not be thrown back in the face of the other parent. Even if it would give you great delight to tell your former spouse "The children really hate your new boyfriend (or girlfriend) and don't even want to come visit your new apartment," don't do it! The exercises were designed to help parents and children rebuild, not as a way to get revenge. If you do use the information gained in the exercises against your adolescent's other parent it will damage your own relationship with your child by seriously destroying trust.

If, however, your son or daughter tells you he or she is addicted to alcohol or drugs or so depressed as to contemplate suicide, you must immediately get professional help. Tell the child that you are going to find a counselor who can help in this situation and that the child must confide in the counselor. In this example, you insist on sharing with someone else the results of an intimate exchange you and your child have had, but only because it is related to the child's survival. In addition, you openly share your action and your reasons for the action with your teenager.

Most people value trustworthiness and honesty. To the adolescent who is beginning to look at the world with critical eyes, it is crucial that you are always honest. If you manipulate facts and events to portray a picture of your divorce or your former spouse that makes you look "all good" and your spouse

14

look "all bad," your adolescent will eventually fit the pieces together and discover your lack of honesty.

At the time of a divorce many children have found that their parents are not "safe" people to talk to. They discover that if they express their ideas and feelings about the divorce, these may be expressions the parents do not want to hear. Parents sometimes try to change the child's thoughts to be more like their own; or a parent's feelings may be so intense that the child feels overwhelmed and frightened. This may create a dilemma for you. When doing the exercises with your teenagers, how expressive will you be about your own feelings? It is always important to be honest with your children, but it is not necessary to tell them all your thoughts on each issue. Along the same lines, if a teenager shares with you how angry he or she feels toward you for filing for the divorce, for example, try to understand and accept his or her need to express that feeling without becoming judgmental or defensive. Perhaps it might help to imagine (or even remember) how angry you might have felt if your mother and father had divorced. (Perhaps they did.) As time goes on and your children understand more about the divorce, they may come to accept and understand it. Then they may no longer feel so angry at you, but continue to feel sad about the loss of the family.

As good as it might feel to have your son or daughter console and support you, that is too big of an emotional task for a twelve- to eighteen-year-old. If you need support or a shoulder to cry on, by all means go find it. Don't burden your teenager with the job, however. He or she has enough to do in dealing with his or her own feelings.

Finally, you will discover that throughout the book parents are encouraged to work toward developing a healthy "co-parenting" relationship for the good of their children. In some instances this is impossible. There are a few parents who, for a number of complex reasons, are unable or unwilling to co-parent. There are even some parents that cannot parent. Occasionally after a divorce, one parent totally disappears from his or her child's life.

If your former spouse shows little or no interest in parenting, you may feel very hurt or angry. Or perhaps you are even happy to have him or her out of your life completely. Regardless of how you feel, however, try not to degrade your former spouse to your children; this type of behavior usually backfires. Generally, the more one parent puts down the other, the more the children dislike the complaining, hostile parent. Children do not like *anyone* talking about either parent in a negative manner. Children want to love both parents, even a parent who has apparently abandoned them. They feel sad and angry enough over the divorce and need help in understanding the new reality—not your feelings to add to theirs.

This does not mean that you have to be a cheerleader for someone you no longer like or respect. Don't be artificial with your children—especially teenagers (they will see right through it)! Try to be somewhat objective in commenting about your former spouse, and allow the children to express their own feelings of sadness and disappointment without adding hostile comments and opinions. In time—with your help, the help of others (including perhaps your former spouse), and perseverance and prayer—your child will come to an emotional acceptance of the divorce and some relationship or at least acceptance of both parents.

BEGINNING TO REBUILD

Use this book to understand yourself, your divorce experience, and your adolescent child. Understand how these three elements are tied together. Remember, the adjustment process will take a considerable period of time. The essential fact to keep in mind is that the path of adjustment is never steady and that you may have to work on it over and over. On the other hand, by the time you finish this book, you may be surprised at how much progress you and your child or children have made.

EXERCISE 1
Putting the Pieces Back Together

FOR THE WHOLE FAMILY

Take a large 11 × 14″ piece of white paper (the size used for large computer printouts). Across the top, write "How I'm Feeling . . ." Put the paper on the refrigerator or a study wall. Have a number of colored markers on the kitchen table or counter. (Make sure the ink doesn't come through the paper, or you may have another joint project when you're finished!) Ask each family member (including younger children and other adults who may live in your home) to write a feeling on the paper whenever they want, using a color that matches the feeling. Tell your children this is a way for your busy family to share with each other.

You might start by writing **MAD** in large red letters—and then at dinner tell your family how mad you felt when you took the car to the garage for repair and found out you needed a brake job after just having the brakes fixed two months ago. A day or two later add another feeling—perhaps this one related to the divorce. You will be modeling for your children how to communicate feelings. You will also be communicating that the divorce process will create feelings, but that there are other events in one's life that are important. Be sure to include some happy, optimistic feelings—if you have them.

Keep the paper up a couple of weeks. Then put a new one up about a month later. Continue to use this method of communicating for about a year, perhaps

17

generating six or eight sheets of feelings. It will be interesting to look back over the year and remember the journey your family experienced.

ONE FAMILY'S EXAMPLE

GLEN (father, 42)	BEN (son, 17)	ROBBIN (daughter, 15)	ABBY (daughter, 12)
Worried	Dad's a nerd	Don't want to play	Can't think of word
Relieved	Cool	Pretty	Pretty
Busy	Worried	Upset	Mad
Happy	Determined	Sad	Sad
Sad	Sad	O.K.	Happy

Comment

Glen saw his three children about three times a month. Visitations could never be on a fixed schedule because the children all had a myriad of activities going on. Glen lived only twenty minutes from his children and former wife, however, so he could pick them up and drop them off easily. Sometimes he would have two for the weekend, return them on Sunday night, and then pick up the other for dinner on Wednesday.

Glen found this exercise very helpful in fostering open communication between himself and his children and between the children themselves. They were in different grades and activities at school and had different friends and peer groups, so even though they all lived together, they often didn't have the time or inclination to share their feelings.

At one end of his large kitchen counter (away from the sink), Glen taped down an 11 × 14″ piece of paper and wrote "How I Am Feeling . . ." and the names of his children and himself across the top. He then put a jar of magic markers next to the paper and started the process by writing the word "worried" under his own name.

The next time his teenagers visited, they asked him what he was worried about, and he told them that he had been worried about his twelve-year-old daughter Abby, who had been running a fever for a couple of days. After that, the children looked forward to reading what fifteen-year-old Robbin called "Dad's thing." Seventeen-year-old Ben was the first to begin to join in, initially writing "Dad's a nerd" under his own name. Robbin wrote "Don't want to play" at first, and Abby wrote "Can't think of word."

Glen kept using the paper for himself. He wrote "Relieved" when Abby's fever went down and "Busy" after a particularly difficult time at work. His children would ask him about his words, and it gave him an opportunity to share his feelings with them. The children began to add their own feelings. Ben wrote "cool" and explained that he felt good about himself. Robbin wrote "pretty," and Abby copied her older sister. One day, Ben wrote "Worried" and

18

shared with his father his concern about getting accepted to college. (It is interesting that Ben chose to express the same feeling that his father had first listed.)

Ben's willingness to share his feelings helped his sisters decide it was acceptable. One rare evening when all three children were at Glen's for dinner, Robbin wrote "Sad" on the paper, and her sister Abby did the same. The girls explained that they were sad their mother and father were no longer together, and this allowed Glen and Ben to share how sad they also felt about the loss of their family.

Glen continued this exercise for a long time. "Dad's thing" became an important method of communication between father and children. By using the process himself and not being discouraged by the initial teenage "put-downs," Glen was able to encourage his children to use the feeling list when they were willing and able.

Note: When a parent gives an adolescent the freedom to express feelings, objectionable words may be used. For example, adolescents often say they are "pissed off" when they are angry. You need to decide how you will react if your teen uses a word that you find objectionable. Think about whether it is more important to be "proper" or more important to be "open and expressive." Your children may test you to see how committed you are to really knowing them. Try to respond honestly, but not judgmentally. You might say, "'Pissed off' isn't my favorite word, but I know what you mean—you mean you were really angry." By responding in this manner you are communicating to your child your standards, but not shutting the child off.

TABLE TALK

Select one of the feelings written on the paper and ask if the family member who wrote the feeling can tell the rest of the family about the circumstances that triggered the feeling. If the person feels safe in sharing, then a general discussion may follow. Some teenagers, however, are reluctant to share. Accept the need to remain quiet, but ask others if they have ever felt "terri-fied" (or whatever the feeling was). Then have a general discussion. If none of the family members responds, you take the lead and share a time when you have had the feeling named.

19

CHAPTER 2

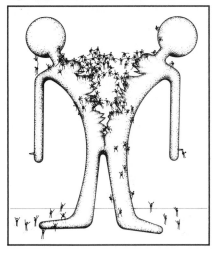

EXPLAINING YOUR DIVORCE TO YOUR CHILDREN

"I know why my parents got divorced, but I'm not telling."

Jim, a twelve-year-old

"I'll never understand why my parents got divorced."

Karen, an eighteen-year-old

Even more than younger children, teenagers need and want to know why their parents divorced. Vague explanations or refusals to discuss the matter will not be acceptable. As they begin to understand the reasons for divorce, however, most adolescents will become more accepting of the changes in their lives.

In many families children have been provided with little information about the divorce. Some parents assume that their teenagers know the "whys" as well as they do themselves. After all, the parents assume, their teens have been a part of the family and have experienced many of the same tensions—often occurring over several years—as the parents. Other parents want to protect their children from experiencing, or even knowing about, unhappy or unpleasant events and therefore decide to tell them very little about the actual reasons for the divorce. Still other parents find the divorce to be so traumatic that it is difficult for them to talk to their children about it at all.

On the other hand, parents sometimes tell their children—especially the older ones—too much about the causes of their divorce. Often when a parent is very hurt and desperately needs a confidant, he or she will turn to a teenager as one would to an adult friend. One eighteen-year-old boy remembers his father taking him for the weekend and spending the entire time complaining about the boy's mother. This same boy was forced to report to his father on all his mother's dates. Although this example may appear extreme, it is not uncommon for a very isolated parent to overinvolve a child.

Neither extreme—"Don't tell the children anything" nor "Get your children on your side"—is what the *children need*.

GUIDELINES

You as a parent can help your child learn about divorce in general, understand specifically what happened in your marriage, and finally help your child mourn, cope with, and accept the loss of the pre-divorce family. Going through this process will probably be helpful for both of you. You may find, as you face these concerns with your adolescent, that both of you will feel less stigmatized by the divorce and will be able to be more open with others.

There are a few basic rules for discussing your divorce with your children:

1. Tell each child what he or she can understand for his or her age and maturity.

The ability to understand, intellectually and emotionally, certain aspects of your divorce will be different for children at different ages. Most four-year-olds can barely understand the concept of divorce; if they even know the word they simply think it means "Daddy and Mommy don't live together." By the time children are six or seven, they may realize that lawyers and courts are involved and that divorce has meant a lot of changes for the family. By age eleven or twelve, children are very interested in how custody is decided. Older high school age children have developed a sense of fairness, and they may want to be sure visitations and custody are equitable.

2. Always tell your child the truth.

When your teen asks you something about the divorce, always answer as honestly and completely as possible—taking into consideration what the particular child can absorb. Fabrications will be discovered sooner or later, and they will only confuse your child about the real reasons for the divorce. Dishonesty about the divorce will also cause your adolescent to doubt your other statements.

3. Do not wait for your child to ask questions; take some initiative.

Teenagers are often reticent about bringing up divorce-related issues or questions. This does not mean they have no questions or don't want more information. It may mean they are taking their cues from you. If you are open, not blaming, and calm in your discussions about the divorce, then pertinent facts, feelings, and information will be shared naturally.

4. Do not use your teenager as an emotional confidant.

Sharing the facts and feelings a child *needs to know* to be able to accept the divorce is not the same thing as discussing everything related to the divorce about which you may have a *need to talk*. When people divorce, they usually need to go over and over the numerous small events that led up to the divorce and to share with someone all of the details of the divorce process. Don't make your children bear this burden. They have enough to deal with already.

DIFFICULT SITUATIONS

Some of the reasons that couples divorce are almost incomprehensible to younger children, but the older, adolescent child may already understand more than you think. Certain situations—including physically or psychologically unhealthy behavior—need to be carefully and lovingly explained to a child in language that he or she can understand.

Helen and Bob had been married for nineteen years and had two daughters, sixteen-year-old Sarah, who was a high school junior, and thirteen-year-old Amy, an eighth grader. The couple had been teenage sweethearts and so much "in love" that they married right after Helen graduated from high school. In the following years, Bob built a successful career as an engineer while Helen stayed home as a full-time homemaker available to their daughters as they grew up.

Everything in the family seemed perfect, except for one development. Bob began to drink excessively, and when he had too much to drink he was often irrational. On several occasions he hit and pushed his wife. For several years, Helen tried to get Bob to see how his drinking was destroying their marriage. They began marriage counseling, but as soon as the counselor began to explore Bob's drinking the husband refused to continue the therapy.

Helen was heartbroken. She wondered if she could continue to live in such a tense, potentially violent, environment. She worried about her daughters witnessing her husband acting out of control. In fact, Sarah's school performance began to suffer. When Sarah confided to Helen that she wasn't bringing any friends home because she didn't want them to see her father so "mean and weird," Helen knew it was time to do something. She filed for a legal separation and got a court order to have Bob removed from the house.

Helen believed both girls were old enough to understand alcoholism. She herself had been attending an ALANON group for the spouses of alcoholics, and following the separation she took Sarah and Amy to join an ALATEEN group. Helen told the girls that Bob's progressive drinking and the accompanying abuse finally had created so much tension in the family that she needed to separate from their father. She told them that their father was basically a good man who refused to recognize that drinking was destroying both himself and his family. She encouraged her daughters to see their father regularly but never to ride in a car with him when he had been drinking.

Sarah attended four ALATEEN session and then decided she didn't want to go to anymore. She felt that with the help of her mother and the group she understood what had happened between her parents. Amy continues to attend ALATEEN meetings and enjoys having a place to talk about her feelings and her parents' separation.

There were no secrets in this family. The two adolescent children were able to realize that their father had an illness and that this was causing the breakup of their parents' marriage. Their mother was able to provide them with needed information and a support group. A younger child might not have been able to comprehend alcoholism in the same way that two teenagers did.

Unpleasant events have almost always preceded the decision to divorce. Sometimes these events or behaviors have had a severely negative impact on children. In these situations it is necessary to help a child work through the facts on a level that he or she can emotionally master. If you were involved, for example, in a love affair before the end of your marriage, your teen might ask, "Did Mike cause you and Dad to get divorced?" You could answer something like this: "I knew Mike and even loved him before Dad and I were divorced, so in some ways knowing Mike probably was one reason we got divorced when we did. But you should know that I was not in love with Dad for two or three years before I even met Mike. Do you want to talk about what caused me to stop loving Dad?"

Do not give children more information than they want to know. Notice in this example that the details of the love affair are not discussed. Adolescents have a difficult time accepting an affair. To them it just doesn't seem fair to the other parent, and they often believe that the parent who had the affair could have avoided it. Regardless of your child's reactions, however, be truthful about what happened.

WHY PARENTS DIVORCE

Our culture encourages a very strong, deeply held conviction that an individual has the right to pursue happiness and to be treated fairly. Because of this, many people now decide to separate or divorce rather than continue to live in an unhappy or unfair marriage. On the other hand, many elements of society also advocate the sanctity and permanence of the marriage commitment, and so many other people choose to live in a less-than-perfect marriage and view divorce as a radical step to be taken only in the most extreme situations—if at all.

There is no "right" answer to this issue for teenagers or other children. For some, living in a loveless, but functional, intact family is preferable to experiencing the upheaval of divorce. It is a proven fact that the family version of musical chairs (changing of families and parents) is extremely detrimental to childhood development. Children need a continuity in their lives with the people who care for them, and they need an environment that is stable and dependable. Just because a child is older, a teenager, does not mean that he or she does not need such a caring environment. In fact, especially during the turbulence of adolescence, a child needs consistent, predictable family interest and support.

The idea of a couple staying together "for the sake of the children" is not always the answer either—even for the children themselves. In most instances when adults live a desolate, conflicted life with their spouse, it affects their relationship with their children. For some people, living in a loveless marriage—being in daily, intimate contact with a person one is supposed to love but does not—becomes a strain of such emotional proportion that divorce becomes the preferable solution for all concerned.

Adolescents are in a stage of life development where they are examining and testing the values and beliefs of society—including the values and beliefs of their parents, their religion, and their school. Your divorce may present a real life-value conflict for your child. "If you said you would remain married until 'death do us part,' how can you divorce Dad because he's boring and stingy?" "If you are getting divorced, does it mean you never were in love?" "Does love really last?" "I want you to be happy—but I want Mom to be happy too." "When I get married it will be forever. This will never happen to me." These are examples of the struggles your teenager may be experiencing.

It is important to convey a willingness to discuss these concerns with your son or daughter. In such discussions, it is important to be emotionally calm, stating your beliefs, but not denigrating your former spouse's values. For example, you may say, "I really thought Dad and I could work out the problems in our marriage, and I guess both of us were partly to blame. I think a marriage commitment is for life, however, but I guess Dad was more unhappy than I was and just felt he couldn't stay married." Notice in the above example the parent states her values clearly, but she does not devalue or run down her former spouse. Also allow your child the freedom to explore and express beliefs that differ from yours.

Thinking about divorce in a general philosophical way is important, for it will help you clarify your own feelings about divorce. It is even more important, however, to examine what happened in your own, specific marriage that resulted in a divorce. Take a few minutes and think back over the years of your marriage. When did you become aware of the problems that grew to be so serious that your marriage was threatened? What steps did you and your former spouse take to try to resolve your differences? Did this help? What was the final "straw" that resulted in the decision to divorce?

The answers to these questions provide information that your adolescent children need to know, but before you share this with them take the time to sort through the process you have been through. Perhaps it would be helpful to write down the answers to these questions or share them with a close friend or relative. However you choose to analyze "what happened to my marriage," complete your own thinking and understanding before discussing it with your child. Do not use your adolescent as an adult friend, however willing he or she may be to fill that role. Remember your adolescent needs to be a teenager and has enough challenges just in mastering his or her own life.

In some divorces the causal factors may be unfortunate and sad but are not of such proportion that the family is left with permanent, deep emotional scars. Janet and Cliff married when they were nineteen and twenty respectively. At the time of their marriage Janet had completed one year of college at a state university, while Cliff, her high school sweetheart, was working as a plumber's apprentice, hoping eventually to become a master plumber. Janet's parents did not want her to marry Cliff because they felt the two young people came from such different backgrounds and that eventually Janet would be unhappy in the marriage.

In fact, that is exactly what happened. When Janet's children entered school full time, she completed college. Then, after seventeen years of marriage and two children (15 and 12), she got a job as a systems analyst with a major corporation. Two years later Janet was promoted to a district manager, which required frequent travel.

Cliff had begun to feel distance grow between them when Janet was attending college. He was hoping she would choose not to work. When she began working, Cliff, in fear of losing her, began to criticize her job, her colleagues, and her interests. He even put down how she dressed. Janet began to feel "who needs this?" but decided to get marriage counseling. The couple struggled in counseling, expressing their honest feelings. Cliff felt he could not tolerate Janet working in a business atmosphere making more money than he. Janet was unwilling to give up a job and life style she enjoyed and had worked for. Both Janet and Cliff felt they had married too young, and both could see they felt more comfortable in life styles that were similar to those of their families of origin. After four months of counseling, they decided to divorce and began planning how they could make this family transition in a way that would cause the least stress for their children.

Although it is sad that Janet and Cliff are divorced, they are one of the fortunate divorcing couples who work together to understand what happened to the marriage and continue to work together on behalf of the children.

Laura and Steve are not as lucky. Laura finally went to see a counselor after she and Steve had been married fourteen years. A sad, terrified Laura slowly revealed a story of years of physical abuse. Laura was ashamed that she had remained in the marriage for so many years, but she had the memory of the caring, fun-loving Steve she dated. She kept hoping that the "old" Steve would reappear. The beatings became more frequent and violent, however, sending Laura to the hospital three times.

Steve was unemployed and more demanding than ever. Laura begged him to begin counseling, but he refused. Finally Laura moved to her parent's home with her twelve-year-old daughter Lisa. She will not, and cannot, talk to Steve. All communication is handled through their attorneys, and all Laura is praying for is to heal emotionally and to be able to support her daughter and herself.

By catching a glimpse into two different divorces, you can see that problems and responses to the problems can be extremely varied. The important fact to remember in explaining your divorce to your teenagers is this: *Children need to know that they did not cause their parents' divorce and that the causes of divorce are adults' problems—not theirs.*

To explain your divorce effectively to your children, you must understand the reasons for it yourself. It takes months or years of serious deliberation and unhappiness before most couples decide to divorce, and even then the reasons are not always clear even to them. Sometimes either the husband or the wife decides that the unhappiness or pain that he or she is experiencing in the marriage is worse than the pain and changes the divorce will bring on everyone involved. It becomes obvious to him or her that divorce is the only solution. It is not always so understandable to the other spouse—or to the couple's children.

Sometimes the decision to divorce is mutual. Both spouses decide the marriage is not working and they come to a divorce settlement amicably. They and their children begin to rebuild a different life, keeping disruptions to a minimum. Such divorces are rare, and even so, the children will experience losses and change.

Most divorces are the result of a complicated process between two people. Each divorce is unique, just as each marriage is unique. It is impossible to list all the reasons why marriages that start out with so much promise end with so much pain. There are, however, several main causes of divorce in the United States—some of which are interrelated. It is the inability of a couple to communicate, compromise, or change on these issues that finally results in the decision that they can no longer fulfill their marriage vows.

Here are ten of the basic causes of divorce I have observed in my research and counseling experience. I make no judgments about their validity in individual situations or about the values of any particular divorcing person. Neither do I offer any options or suggestions for how to save a marriage. This book assumes that a separation or divorce is a fact and concentrates on the effects on the children.

1. Personality Differences.

All people are different from each other psychologically. They have different personalities. Some people like things very neat and organized and become upset and even angry if anything is out of place. Other people are relaxed and productive in a messy home or office. Some are energetic in the morning, and others like to stay up late and really begin to come alive about ten or eleven at night. Some people need to share the details of daily living with others, while others may not like to talk very much. There are people who like cold climates, others hot. There are those who like to socialize with groups, while others prefer solitary types of activities. Some people require a lot of approval and praise, and some do not seem to care what others think.

These kinds of differences make us unique and interesting to each other. Your personality was formed by the interaction of many influences: where you lived growing up, how your parents related to you and to each other, your health, your own biological makeup, how friends and teachers related to you and how you related to them, and whether you had brothers and sisters. These are just a few of the factors that influenced the formation of your personality. When you married, you assumed that your spouse was someone you could live with comfortably for the rest of your life.

When you live with someone intimately for a long time, however, you really begin to know his or her personality. As your mate's personality became known, perhaps you discovered differences that began to bother you. At first these differences may have appeared to be little annoyances. As time went on, however, these differences may have become more and more troublesome, until you finally felt you could no longer live with your partner.

Some people—and your adolescent children may be among them—believe that such relatively minor differences do not justify divorcing. Many have discovered, however, that personality and psychological compatibility is at the core of a close marital relationship. Your teenagers might be capable of understanding this because they probably spend considerable time analyzing friendships. By the time most children reach junior high, they have developed an awareness of the "type" of person they like for a friend. You can illustrate the differences between you and your former spouse by pointing out somewhat parallel "mismatches" in your adolescents' friendship networks.

2. Value Differences.

Just as each person has a unique personality, everyone has developed a philosophical stance on life that reflects his or her individual values and beliefs. What a person values and believes is very influential in the way he or she chooses to live life.

One person may value security and frugality. For this person, saving money by using discount coupons or buying things "on sale," staying at the same job, and owning a home and sticking close to it may be very important. Another person may value spontaneity and fun. This person may enjoy taking exotic vacations, going out often and staying late, making "impulse" purchases and not wanting the responsibility of having children. A person may believe mankind is basically good; this person will be trusting and hopeful. Another person may believe most people are basically "bad" and thus be suspicious and on guard around others. When married people discover that some of their fundamental values or beliefs are not shared by their partners, disagreements and arguments may begin to fester.

Money issues are frequently cited as a reason for divorce. Couples fight about not having enough money or how money is to be spent. Below the surface of these recurring disagreements are usually different values not only about money but about work and social status. These differences about the meaning of money often carry over after the divorce and can affect children directly by creating a value conflict within themselves over the relative value of material possessions.

Religious differences are often a cause of marital problems. Sometimes varied doctrines or customs are the direct cause of friction. More often, the difficulties are less a matter of denominational affiliation or practice than they are different levels of fervor and involvement in religious activity.

Child rearing itself is another area of strong values and beliefs. One spouse may believe, for example, that it is important to give a child wide exposure to extracurricular activities, such as dancing, sports, or scouts, while the other may feel that it is dangerous for a child to be overinvolved in such activities. One may forbid dating before sixteen, the other may feel it is good for younger teens to have boyfriends or girlfriends. One may be pro-allowance, another opposed to giving children money unless it is earned.

It is very difficult to change someone's values. No one changes them as the result of an argument with a spouse. People decide to get divorced because they learn over time that their ideas on a wide variety of matters are significantly different from those of their spouse and because they are unwilling or unable to compromise on or respectfully accept their differences. Children are often caught in this conflict both before and after the divorce. Adolescence is a time when family and personal values are being re-examined, and so your teenager might be very open to understanding the difference in values between you and your former spouse without making value judgments or siding with either parent.

3. Another Person.

Many marriages end in divorce when one of the partners falls in love with another person. When this happens the partner who has been left usually feels devastated. The parent with the new relationship will want the children to know and like his or her new love partner, and the "new couple" may want to include the children in activities. The other, "dumped," parent often feels rage and contempt for the third party and may try to recruit the children on his or her side.

When one partner falls in love with someone else, it is usually because there were already considerable personality and value differences in the marriage. For at least one spouse, the relationship was already dead. Adolescents, however, are exploring the very concepts of love and fidelity. Many have very idealistic hopes for marriage, and accepting the reality that their parents fell out of love is very difficult for them.

4. Excessive Drinking and Abuse of Drugs.

Substance abuse is a disease that touches many families. This illness may contribute to the events leading up to the divorce. Excessive drinking or drug use often result in violence, automobile accidents, loss of employment, and physical illness. There are, however, many substance abusers who do not miss work and are never violent, yet their drinking or drug consumption does numb their feelings. They remove themselves emotionally from the family, being unavailable as a companion, friend, parent, or lover.

Most teenagers have had alcohol and drug education in school, so they may be well aware of the signs and consequences of substance abuse. This may not make them any less upset by its occurrence in their family, and it may make them especially nervous about their own possible tendency toward addiction. They may also abuse alcohol or drugs as a way of getting back at one or both of their parents for doing the same thing.

5. Physical, Sexual, or Emotional Abuse.

There are people who have low self-esteem, who are quick to anger and easily frustrated. In a marriage, these people can become abusive to their mates and/or children. In many cases, this tendency can be traced to their own childhood experience of abuse or neglect. Regardless of the reason a person is abusive, it is always damaging for both the other spouse and the children to remain in such a situation.

The most common type of abuse occurs when men—who are stronger and have been given cultural messages of superiority—abuse a woman. There are women, however, who have been excessively cruel and abusive to their passive husbands. Another sad pattern is when one or both parents are abusive to their children. When there is such abuse in a family, adolescents may begin to fight back or to run away. Such behavior might require special counseling to uncover the reasons for the reaction or to cope with the effects of the abuse.

If you or your adolescent were abused during your marriage, it is important to provide the opportunity to discuss the fear and rage felt at those times and also to share the sense of sadness and relief when the family finally separated to become safe.

6. Job Conflict.

Excessive job or career demands on one or both partners or conflicting employment choices sometimes place stress on the marital relationship. Sometimes one spouse or the other will put all his or her energy into work, leaving little for the family. In the extreme, this can become the disease of "workaholism." The need to move with a job—especially from city to city—or to travel extensively can add to the pressures on a marriage. Sometimes just conflicting work schedules—necessary and unavoidable—are enough to destroy the relationship that exists between a couple.

For teenagers, who are just beginning to consider what kind of work they might like to do in their lives, this kind of conflict can be especially difficult. Some may react by adopting the very traditional position that the wife should stay at home while the husband pursues his career, while others (especially the adolescent girls) may decide that they should not marry at all if they want to work outside the home.

Another special problem caused by work conflict can arise when one parent has been away from home excessively. In this situation, an adolescent may have been pulled into serving as a surrogate partner for the "at home" spouse. When a separation or divorce between the parents finally takes place, there may also have to be an adjustment in the relationship between teenager and parent. Children who have become an emotional partner to a parent need to be released from that role so they can become their own person.

7. Financial Pressures.

Decline or loss of family income or assets may prove to be too much pressure for the marriage to endure. The loss of money does not in and of itself cause the divorce. It is rather the stress caused by constant confrontation by bill collectors, bankruptcy, or the loss of the family home or apartment, which can result in a loss of self-esteem and increased family instability.

Most adolescents want to "keep up" with their friends and may have put pressure on their parents to spend funds unnecessarily. After a divorce, these teenagers can feel that they are partly to blame for the family's financial problems and therefore for their parents' divorce. Some teens may even feel it is their responsibility to bring more money into the family—even to the point of working too many hours or even quitting high school altogether in order to work. It is important in these situations to assure the children that family money problems are not their concern and to encourage them to concentrate on their schooling.

8. Homosexuality or Bisexuality.

People with homosexual or bisexual leanings sometimes marry and even have children. As the years pass, these people may experience the stress of not being able to express their true sexual longings. Sometimes the desire to be more honest about their sexual preference results in the termination of their marriage. Such a situation can cause special identity problems for children— especially teenagers, who are in the midst of the process of defining their own sexual identities. In these cases, the needs of the children to establish their own sexuality must take precedence over the desire of their parents to promote or condemn an alternative life style.

9. Immaturity.

Some couples marry young—before their adult personalities have formed and before they have had an opportunity to experience a variety of social experiences. These people were simply not mature enough to make the lifelong commitment of marriage and have not been able to grow together. It often happens that one partner may mature emotionally or intellectually while the other remains basically the same as when they were married. At about the age of thirty or thirty-five, one or both of the partners may simply feel trapped in the marriage and want to get out. The prospect of living forty more years in an unfulfilling marriage seems unbearable.

To family, friends, and even their children, this may not appear to be a good reason to divorce. Adolescents seem especially quick to take a judgmental

32

stance on this issue. Many have a romanticized view of love and marriage and cannot conceive of the possibility of a couple making a youthful mistake. Since they are young themselves, they cannot imagine that decisions made at a young age can prove to be unworkable.

10. Mental Illness.

When one partner has a serious mental illness, such as schizophrenia, the other partner may decide to divorce so that he or she can build a life with more stability. In these situations, the healthy spouse may feel guilty deserting a mentally ill person, and the children might even blame that spouse for being unfaithful. It may, however, be the only step possible to create a healthy environment for the healthy spouse and the couple's children.

Adolescents are fully capable of understanding mental illness. They may, however, harbor fears that the illness of a parent might somehow be passed on to them. In these cases, it would be helpful to have a mental health professional discuss the parent's illness with all the children and be available to answer questions and provide assurances about the children's own mental health.

* * *

Teenagers can understand to some degree all of the above reasons for their parents' divorce. What is most important is that the reasons be presented to each child individually and geared to the child's age and maturity. Explanations should be done in an honest manner yet without giving more details than are requested or can be handled. This takes some initiative and skill on the part of the parent.

If both you and your former spouse basically see the reasons for the divorce in the same way, your children will be receiving similar messages from each of you about the reasons for the divorce. If you see the deterioration process of your marriage very differently, your children will, of course, be receiving conflicting messages. Your teen may even conclude that one of you is lying, when actually both of you are basically telling the truth from your own perspectives. In that case, your teenage children may need extra help in making sense of why two people they trust and love think so differently.

EXERCISE 2
The Many "Whys" of Divorce

FOR YOU

Take a piece of paper, and across the top write "Why We Divorced (or Separated)." Along the side of the paper write your name and your former spouse's name. Using the categories described in this chapter, write down what you think each of you would perceive as the major factors contributing to the divorce, listing them in order of importance. Of course, you cannot be sure of exactly how your former spouse perceives the causes of the divorce, but since the two of you have dealt with each other extensively concerning divorce issues, you should have a good idea about his or her perceptions. After citing what you and your former spouse think are the major factors leading to the divorce, see what—if any—are major differences between your perceptions. If there are differences that may be continuing to cause conflicts/ tension write down any ideas you might have about how you can make the post-divorce atmosphere and adjustment easier for your teenager.

HELEN'S EXAMPLE
WHY WE ARE SEPARATED
My reasons:

1. Physical Abuse.

Bob's violent outbursts were unpredictable and becoming more frequent. I often felt tense and worried. The girls were also worrying about how their dad would respond.

2. Alcohol Abuse.

I am not sure whether Bob's physical abuse of me was caused by his drinking, but he was always drunk when one of these outbursts occurred. He is drinking more and more, and I know that on some days he is now drinking on his lunch hour as well as in the evening.

3. Immaturity.

Perhaps we married too young. I was only eighteen and a half. Bob used to drink while we were dating and after we were married, but for the first ten years of our marriage there didn't seem to be a problem. Bob's father was a heavy drinker, though, and used to slap his wife, so maybe I should have seen that the potential was there.

My former husband's (Bob's) reasons:

1. Personality Differences.

Helen just has to be the boss. She always thinks she is right. She pushes me so hard that sometimes I lose my temper. I'm always sorry and she always said she forgave me—at least until she moved out.

2. Value and Belief Differences.

I don't see anything wrong with social drinking. Helen likes her glass of wine when we go out to dinner. Now she acts as if someone who likes to drink is automatically an alcoholic.

3. Career Conflicts.

Helen just doesn't appreciate how much pressure I am under at work. Sure I sometimes take a drink at lunch, but only when I am with a client and they want a drink. I also like a beer when I get home. It helps me relax.

IDEAS TO HELP SARAH AND AMY

Bob and I really do look at the breakup of our marriage very differently. I believe that the central problem is his denial of the impact of alcohol on his behavior. In his heart, I believe he knows that his drinking is out of control, but he just is not ready to quit, and so I feel that a separation is the only solution. If he were to stop drinking, I don't know what I would do.

Going to ALATEEN has already helped Sarah and Amy. They now understand that alcoholism is an illness, and they are much less judgmental of their father. I will continue to go to ALANON and encourage the girls to learn as much as they can about the effects of Bob's drinking on them.

If Bob tells them that I am bossy or a prude who doesn't approve of drinking, I will simply reply "That is how your dad makes sense of what is going on, but I believe the main problems have to do with his drinking. I am sure there are things I've done that bother Dad, too. If your dad stopped drinking, we would all have to try working at being a family again, but there are other problems in our relationship that would have to be dealt with. Right now, however, Dad is not ready to stop drinking, and I have decided that we cannot live with him anymore."

I will not argue with Bob or the girls about how he views the separation, nor will I run him down. This may help them not feel that they have to take sides between us. I think it is good to slowly indicate to them that even if Bob stopped drinking I doubt if we will get back together. They need to understand that my emotional distance from their father is a result of many years of disappointment, although I don't think that I need to go into detail about the physical abuse.

Comment

This exercise was done by the woman mentioned in the first example in this chapter. As Helen did this exercise, she realized how painful the breakup of the marriage must be for her husband. She also became aware of the fact that even if Bob stopped drinking, she was doubtful that they could rekindle their marriage. She knew that she must tell the girls this, or otherwise they would have the impression that the alcoholism was the only problem.

Helen also realized that she could have foreseen some of the problems in their marriage if she had looked at Bob's parents and their relationship. She realized how immature she had been when they had gotten married. As she tried to imagine how Bob would explain their separation, Helen realized that she really did not know what Bob thought. She did understand, however, that he would try to put most of the blame on her and that she should not react when he did.

Helen believed that the progressive illness of alcoholism had pushed her emotionally away from Bob, and thought that if he gave up drinking she might give the marriage another try. After completing the exercise, however, she was no longer certain that she wanted to be married to him, sober or drinking. This helped her admit that she too had a role in the breakup of her family.

EXERCISE FOR AGES 12-14

Get four sheets of paper. Paste a picture of yourself on one sheet, a picture of your former spouse on another, and a picture of your teenager on the third. On the fourth sheet write:

Dear _____,
These three people all have different ideas about the divorce. Under each picture, please write what you think each one believes caused the divorce. After you have done this, let's talk about it. Remember, it is O.K. for each of us to see the divorce differently.

Love,
Mom (or Dad)

Place the four sheets of paper on your teen's pillow. Be prepared for groans and being told how stupid this is. Some adolescents will do the exercise, and others will at least think about it. Be prepared to discuss the reasons for the divorce if your child decides he or she want to discuss it, but let him or her bring it up.

EXERCISE FOR AGES 15-18

Ask your teenager to go for a "talk and walk" with you. If it is too cold to walk outside, go to a large indoor mall. On the walk, tell your son or daughter that when families go through a divorce, it is normal for every member of the family to have a different perspective of what happened. Briefly explain your view of the divorce and tell your child that your former spouse will almost certainly understand and explain the breakup differently. Encourage him or her to talk with the other parent about this topic.

Let your adolescent know that you are interested in his or her perspective on the divorce, but do not pressure for an answer. If he or she starts to give an opinion, it is critical that you not react defensively or immediately begin to restate your own position. Just listen for a change, your teenager will be so surprised and grateful!

TABLE TOPICS

1. What are the major reasons that people you know (family, friends, parents of friends, relatives, neighbors) have gotten divorced? Discuss the variety of reasons.
2. Are there any reasons that people get divorced that are not good reasons? What are they?
3. Are there any valid reasons for getting divorced? What are they?

CHAPTER 3

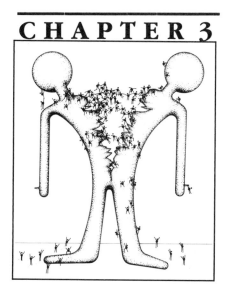

DIVORCE MEANS MANY CHANGES

"I wish my friends knew how hard it is to have divorced parents—especially ones that don't get along."

Jenelle, a fourteen-year-old

Although almost one-third of the children in the United States will spend some time in a single-parent household, when parents divorce it often feels to a teenager that his or her family is the only one experiencing this fate. Jenelle lives in a community where divorce is not uncommon. Her parents have been divorced over two years, yet she continues to feel "different" and "odd." Jenelle's reaction was similar to Sam's, another adolescent whose parents recently divorced.

Sam lived in Jenelle's community and attended a neighboring high school. Sam's father Alex was an open, caring man. He was participating in a divorce support group to help rebuild a life for himself and his three adolescent children. When Alex spoke of Sam, he painted a picture of a well-adjusted, happy teenager. Sam was on the soccer team and his grades were consistently B's or C's. It all sounded great to the counselor and the other divorced parents in Sam's group.

Five months after the divorce group ended, however, Alex went to an open house at Sam's high school and discovered that Sam was now failing almost every subject. When Alex suggested to the soccer coach that perhaps Sam was reacting to his parents' divorce, the coach was surprised. Sam had not told anyone about the divorce or the fact that his mother had moved five hundred miles away.

Alex went home to talk with Sam about the concerns raised by his teachers. Sam burst into angry tears when he discovered his father had told his coach and teachers about the divorce. "How could you do this, Dad? I didn't want anyone to know. Now they will all know I'm different."

Jenelle feels different, Sam was afraid his teachers and friends would see him as different. Most adolescents desperately want to "fit in," to be like the other teens. In reality, Jenelle's and Sam's family structure (parents divorced, children living primarily with one parent, visiting the other) was shared by hundreds of other students in their respective high schools. Yet each perceived that he or she was different from everyone else.

Both Jenelle and Sam needed their parents' help in understanding the reality of divorce and the changes it precipitated in their young lives. Many changes affect all family members when parents divorce. Some of these changes create major losses: family home, a livable income, a shoulder to cry on. Other changes are so small that they might even go unrecognized: changes in routine, abandonment of a shared hobby, lack of help with the dishes or homework.

Because of escalating social and technological changes, people need the physical, emotional, economic, and spiritual anchor of a stable family more than ever. Many members of divorcing families feel the loss of their family identity. Adults experience a vague yet deep sadness that comes from the disruption of family roots. Children wonder "Am I an Anderson or a Caldwell?" Mom takes back her maiden name—often only to change it again if she remarries.

If you have adolescent children you have probably been married for a number of years—perhaps twenty or more. This means as a couple, and as a family, you have experienced much of life together. You have established rituals and routines, ways to celebrate holidays, vacations, and birthdays. You have made decisions about where and how to live. At every turn in your life there are reminders of your family. This is also true for your teenager. Part of your responsibility as a parent is to deal with these changes yourself so that you can be helpful to your children in learning to adjust to the new situation.

BOTH PARENTS AS EMOTIONAL GUIDES

You are now engaged in rebuilding a family that consists of three interrelated parts: you and your children; your children and your former spouse; and you and your former spouse as co-parents. When a child is born, he or she is totally dependent upon others to see that she or he survives. As each year

40

passes, a child will be able to do more and more things for himself or herself, until at some magical age between eighteen and twenty-one the child becomes a true adult. All children, however, even adult children, never outgrow the desire for parental concern and love.

Children of high school age—between the ages of twelve and eighteen—are already well on their way to adulthood. They spend at least six or seven hours a day away from home at school and several more with friends and at part-time jobs. They select their own clothes, have strong opinions on music and entertainment, can (if they wish) clean and cook and even sew. The adolescent still, however, looks to his or her parents to provide a secure, safe home base from which to venture out into the new and exciting world of *independence.*

Teenagers still want parent and home to be there when needed—even if they seem to communicate the exact opposite by most of their words and actions! They need someone to cheer them up; encourage their efforts at school, job, sports, or the arts; be concerned about their friends, curfews, alcohol, and drug use; uphold a certain code of values and ethics even as they test it; and generally care about *them.* They are counting on their parents to be there. A teenage child in a real and special way needs the interest, help, concern, and love of both parents—a mother and a father—if at all possible. Divorce is especially difficult because it disrupts this unstated need.

When parents divorce, the child usually lives with one parent—referred to legally as the "custodial" parent. This parent has the legal right to make major decisions about the child. The other parent, the "non-custodial" parent, usually has visitation rights. These visitation patterns vary, and may range from several visits a week with the children to one long stay in the summer. Many parents are able to work out a visitation schedule that feels equitable to them and is comfortable for the children—although for many teenagers, nothing that disrupts their personal schedule is "comfortable."

In our society, the mother has usually been granted custody of the children. Fathers are increasingly questioning this practice, asserting that they can perform the role of a primary, nurturing parent as well as the mother. In fact, some fathers have been named the custodial parent. Another variation is what is called "joint custody," with each parent having input into major decisions and the children spending blocks of time with each parent. Many states now encourage parents to consider joint custody in the hope that it will help the children of divorce have a positive relationship with both parents.

Adolescents usually have very strong opinions about their living arrangements and visitations. If they are well established in a particular school and community, they often wish to remain there—regardless of which parent is granted custody. For teenagers, activities at school and with peers are often a paramount concern, and visitation schedules must be kept flexible to take these feelings into account.

If you are the non-custodial parent, it may take dedication on your part to keep up contact with your adolescent child. Some days he or she may not sound all that happy even to talk to you. Your son or daughter may not share little bits of news like in the "old days," and you may often get the feeling that he or she would rather be anywhere else than talking with you. Your feelings are probably accurate. *Yet such actions are not necessarily abnormal for any teenager nor aimed specifically at you.* If you were still living with your child, many times he or she would grab something to eat, go to his or her room, turn on the stereo, and call a friend. This is normal behavior for all teens—whether their parents are divorced or not. So when a teenager is engaged in his or her own world, a call from a non-custodial parent—no matter how missed or loved—is an interruption. In this situation, moreover, your call may be an intruding reminder that you no longer live there. This does not mean you shouldn't call—*you should*—for phone calls tell your child that you remember, you care. You are the adult parent meeting your teenager's needs—your child is not yet grown up enough to take care of you.

If you are the custodial parent, you may worry that when your adolescent is away visiting the other parent he or she will be exposed to values or behavior of which you do not approve. For example, the other parent may allow your teenager to watch R-rated movies or even have a glass of beer or wine with dinner at home. *Keep in mind that an adolescent will have many experiences that will not be exactly what you would select.* The fact that some of these experiences might happen with your former spouse should not magnify them out of proportion. You may even find that your child "likes" the non-custodial parent better because of such loosening of the rules. Try not to become overly nervous about what your teen does when visiting the other parent. Your teenager will be an adult soon enough and will sort out which of the values he or she wishes to live by no matter what you say.

Some custodial parents are so embittered because of the hurt experienced in the breakup of the marriage that they do not want their children to have any contact with the non-custodial parent. This merely complicates things for the children. A cardinal axiom of parenting the children of a divorce is this: *Children want to know and love both parents.* If you care for your children, try to put your own hurts aside and allow and even encourage them to know and continue to care for their other parent. When your children have grown they will thank you for understanding and permitting this open relationship.

Occasionally there is a parent who is so emotionally unstable that it might truly endanger a teenager to spend time alone with him or her. Parents who might fall into this dangerous category are chemically dependent people who drink or abuse drugs when children are around or parents who have been sexually, physically, or emotionally abusive. If you suspect your former spouse fits one of these categories, discuss it with your attorney. Visitations may be arranged in a controlled environment. A note of caution: some parents hate their former spouse so much they unjustly accuse him or her of being abusive or alcoholic in an attempt to control visitation. This type of vindictive behavior meant to distance and perhaps protect your child can easily backfire on you. It will only cause further damage to your teenager, and you run the risk of losing his or her respect and confidence.

YOUR CHILD'S AGE AND RESPONSE TO YOUR DIVORCE

Your child should be of junior or senior high school age now. When you two have completed the exercises in this book (and other exercises you may create), it does not mean the subject of parental divorce has been dealt with and you can now forget about it. Children need to work and rework their parents' divorce. This process will continue throughout their lives. The understanding of a twelve-year-old is very different from that of an eighteen-year-old—which differs again from what is needed by a twenty-four-year-old—or even a forty-year-old.

As children approach important developmental periods they often need to bring up aspects of the divorce again and again. For example, if your child was eleven when you got divorced, he or she will probably need to spend some time rethinking the divorce at age sixteen. This is the age when children are beginning to date and examine intimate relationships. They are dealing with issues of sexuality and identity. Children of both sexes at this age want to know what went wrong in their parent's marriage. Teenagers who have been living with one parent may contemplate changing custody at this time. They may need to know what the other parent is really like. Such reconsideration of the divorce may take place again when a child leaves home, when he or she begins to contemplate marriage, and again around the time his or her own children are about the same age your child was when you divorced.

LOSSES THAT ACCOMPANY DIVORCE

Here are some of the losses that adolescents may experience when divorce disrupts their families:

1. Loss of a Dream.

When people marry, they usually believe it will be forever. They have a picture in their heads of the happy family they will become. When this fails to come to pass it is very sad. "If I can't count on my belief in marriage what can I count on?"

Teenagers also have a dream, a dream of the ideal family they would like to be a part of, the ideal mother and the ideal father. Of course no real-life parent can fill the ideal, but when parents divorce there is the crushing proof that the child does not have the longed-for family or the perfect parents. This splash of reality can be especially jarring at this idealistic age.

2. Loss of Self-Esteem.

When a marriage relationship does not work out, the divorcing partners often feel as if they have failed. "What did I do wrong? Why doesn't she love me anymore? Is there something wrong with me or with my judgment? Am I lovable?" Pondering these questions is normal when reflecting on divorce, but the result may be a lowering of self-esteem.

The child, who is continuing biological proof of the marriage, is also at risk of experiencing lower self-esteem. This tendency is even greater during the teen years, when self-esteem can sink very low in any case.

"How can my parents, whom I respected and trusted, not resolve their problems? I must not be able to solve problems either." If one parent continues to criticize the other parent it hurts the child. The child is always the child of both parents regardless of how despicable the parent has been.

3. Loss of Caring Relationships.

Divorce disrupts relationships in the family. Relationships that may be ruptured are not only the spousal relationship (although that is the most obvious), but the relationship between parent and child may change. For example, non-custodial fathers often feel a sense of estrangement from their children, children feel they must monitor what they say to each parent, and custodial mothers may have less time to spend with each child because of the need to work and provide all the home care tasks.

Extended family contacts—grandparents, aunts/uncles, cousins, family friends—may all become strained, revised, or even eliminated as segments of the previously whole family decide with whom they can/will remain connected. As holidays and birthdays come and go it is often painfully obvious to all family members that things are not the same. To a teenager just beginning to sort out these relationships on an adult level, this loss can seem greater than to anyone else.

4. Loss of a Problem or Emotional Pain.

Divorce is an attempt to eliminate a serious problem. Why would anyone—especially a teenager who seems to feel that the world is full of problems—feel a loss when a divorce allows at least some measure of resolution of an intolerable situation? When we live with someone for a long time, we establish patterns that become very familiar; even painful patterns lend security to a way of life. "The devil you know is often better than the one you don't." A husband married to an alcoholic wife, for example, is accustomed to feeling tense and worried as he approaches home. The children are similarly accustomed to never being able to bring friends home and to assuming adult responsibility for cooking and cleaning.

If this family divorces, with father and children establishing a well-cared for, structured environment free of alcohol and drugs, all parties—especially the adolescents—may feel a loss of the old ways. There may be a subtle pull to recreate the familiar, painful home. After all, it was what they all knew for so long, and everyone was used to the chaos. With the source of tension removed, all members of this family might feel a sense of loss to go with their relief. (Of course they would also be feeling sad that the mother is still ill.)

5. Loss of Home, Neighborhood, School.

Moving is always a crisis (big or little) for a family, because it requires an adjustment to a new environment. For a teenager, such a change can appear to be cataclysmic—whether a divorce is involved or not. Thus, when a family is forced to sell their home because the parents cannot afford to keep the home following a divorce, teenagers may feel especially disrupted, resentful, and angry.

A change of residence that results in a teenager being forced to attend a different school makes such a move even worse. By the time a child is in junior high, and certainly by high school, most peer groups have crystallized. It can become increasingly difficult for a teen to make new friends. (Of course, we all know of an instance in which a family moved in a child's senior year of high school and it turned out to be the best thing that ever happened to him or her. This is the exception!)

6. Loss of Financial Security and Position.

A large percentage of the poor in our country are single mothers with children. When a family has been supported primarily by the father's income, and then if the husband remarries, this income must help support two homes, and both families suffer. It is usually, however, the mother and the children from the first marriage who suffer most.

Some fathers even feel happy their former wives are suffering. "After all," the reasoning goes, "if my wife was so dumb and uncaring to want a divorce from me she deserves to suffer." Apparently overlooked by this incensed father is the fact that his children are also suffering. Some fathers push this line of thought one step further: they feel that, if the children want a financially secure life, they can simply come live with the father. This is true financial and emotional blackmail! This line of thinking demonstrates no understanding or caring for the needs or feelings of the children. It is, however, an extremely possessive and punishing attitude that some men appear to enjoy.

This is not to advocate that all children should live with their mothers or to suggest that all fathers are punitive. In many divorcing families the children live with the father, usually by mutual choice. Many fathers consistently pay child support and even go above the court-ordered requirement to provide for their children's well-being.

The financial circumstances of the post-divorce family is important, however, because it is a factor that affects the well-being of all family members. Adolescents are remarkably self-centered. (This is okay at this point in their life because they are spending so much effort figuring out who they are.) Thus, a teenager may appear upset over financial losses of the family more than any other loss. "You mean I can't get my designer jeans! I hate you and Dad for doing this to me!" Statements like this are not uncommon.

If your child focuses on the financial ramifications of the divorce it does not mean he or she is devoid of other feelings about the divorce. It just illustrates one way adolescents cope with all of the changes brought about by the divorce. They may focus on the loss that has the most obvious, concrete effects on them, repressing other feelings that are too painful to manage.

All these general categories of loss appear to be experienced in some manner by most divorcing family members. How the family deals with them is what is really important.

COPING AND MOURNING

Your teenager will often need to talk about the divorce in order to understand, accept, and mourn the loss of family. This may sound as if he or she will be just waiting anxiously to pour out questions and feelings. Nothing could be further from the truth! Most adolescents develop techniques to cope with all the changes. They develop and cling to a style that works for them, that saves them pain.

Some common psychological terms used to describe methods of coping are
- "denial" (the divorce is not happening, or the divorce is not sad)
- "repression" (I refuse to think about the divorce)
- "sublimation" (I will become so busy with swimming I won't have to deal with the divorce)

- "projection" (this divorce is the fault of Dad's secretary; she's the villain)

These coping processes are often done subconsciously, so the child is usually unaware of how he or she copes.

Perhaps as you have been reading about these common coping mechanisms of children you may recognize ones you yourself use to help you deal with difficult, painful problems. These psychological techniques are useful for a period of time until a person—child or adult—is strong enough to be able to explore carefully and slowly the dynamics of why a marriage ended. They must not be allowed to go on forever, however, and you as a parent have an obligation to help your children recognize and break through them.

Begin by looking—really looking—at the changes brought about by your divorce. Look at wedding pictures, the marriage license, baby pictures, the family photo album. Remember gifts given at a happier time, holidays, vacations, family routines. As you look at your history, remember the good times and remember the not-so-good times. It is important to recall both aspects of the marriage—so you can feel how the marriage really was. If you feel like crying, go ahead. If you feel like screaming, go ahead (within reason). Share some of your losses, and how you feel about the divorce, with a good friend or close adult relative.

If you cannot look at your past right now, wait a week or two, or a month or two, until you are able to do it. Perhaps you can only think about one memory at a time. That is perfectly all right. Proceed with mourning the loss of your marriage (and "mourning" is what you will be doing) in your own way and at your own pace. You will need to mourn in some way, at some time, however. Don't put it off forever. If you never feel ready to examine your marriage, then perhaps talking with a professional counselor or trusted member of the clergy will help you get started. You need to mourn to help yourself heal, which will result in your being more available to your adolescent.

Your teenager will also be in a process of mourning the loss of the family. When he or she says "Remember how Dad always brought home fresh donuts on Sunday?" know that this is a form of mourning. Remembering the family as it was to him or her (and this may be very different from how you remember the marriage/family) is an important first step in accepting the changes and losses. Perhaps your child will be able to express how he or she feels about some of the changes. "I hate it that you have to work now!" or "Every time I see Mom's new boyfriend I feel sick" are examples of natural expressions of loss. Allow your teen to make these statements. Just as you might need time before feeling able to express your losses, so too your child might need time. Create an open atmosphere and eventually your children will feel free to share the important losses with you.

47

If your feelings are similar to your adolescent's you may offer understanding by stating them. "It's difficult for me to see your Mom with Nick, too." Do not, however, get into a blame/hate campaign. This will eventually be counter-productive. Any time a person carries excessive bitterness and anger it hurts him or her as well as the other people close to the embittered person.

If your feelings differ from those of your child, acknowledge how you feel, but accept how he or she feels. "You know, I sort of enjoy working full time. The responsibility they have given me at work is making me feel good about myself. I know what you mean about missing our time together, though." Notice that this mother did not try to talk her child out of her feelings. She understood and accepted the child's position, even if she did not share the feeling. If you are ever tempted to say "You shouldn't feel that way," stop. There are no "shoulds" about feelings; feelings just exist.

DANGEROUS COPING TECHNIQUES

Examining the history of your marriage and experiencing the many losses is an important step in healing. However, you and your children cannot stop the world and sit around and mourn; you must live each day. You must pay bills, buy groceries, go to school/work, be friends or neighbors, visit relatives, watch T.V., and read newspapers. As you go about daily living, you will find some activities are more enjoyable than others. During the healing process you may find yourself doing more of whatever gives you comfort. For example, during a divorce many adults often talk to friends on the phone more frequently and for longer periods of time than previously. Other methods of coping include getting new clothes, playing new music, eating different foods, and going on a diet. These are positive activities that may help you feel better during a stressful time.

There are coping techniques that are not healthy. These are "overindulgent" responses: overeating, excessive use of alcohol, too much sleep, etc. If you find yourself engaging in behavior that is potentially harmful to your health or well-being, please get professional help. Just talking with an outside party may help you develop better ways of coping.

Adolescents will also be using coping techniques to emotionally manage all of the losses and changes in their lives. There are many functional ways of coping—putting extra effort and time into a sport, watching T.V., spending more time with friends, or trying for the honor roll. Be alert, however, for ways of coping that may be dangerous for your teen. Drinking and drug use are two common responses to loss that some adolescents use. Familiarize yourself with the signs of substance abuse. If you are not aware of the signs, speak with the school counselors—they will probably have printed resources readily available.

Other potentially dangerous coping techniques are developing an eating disorder (anorexia or bulimia), engaging in excessive sexual activity, shoplifting, or practicing a "cultlike" religion, such as satanism. Sometimes parents are the last to know about the destructive behavior in which their child is engaging. Don't become overalarmed, but don't be naive either. Keep your eyes and ears open. Know your children, be aware of their activities and friends. If you suspect problem behavior, immediately speak with a professional mental health worker—psychiatrist, social worker, or psychologist.

When coping techniques begin to fail, that is, when a person no longer feels good no matter what he or she tries, there is a state of depression. Symptoms of depression are sleep disturbance (too much or too little), early waking (about 3 A.M.), eating problems (too much or too little), muscle aches or headaches, exhaustion, and a general sense of sadness with outbursts of weeping.

Divorce may trigger depression for adolescents, although it is important to keep in mind that many adolescents whose parents never even consider divorce experience depression. If you or your child has a number of the above symptoms consult your family physician, and follow his or her recommendations.

ADAPTING

After a period of time you and your children will settle down into a new pattern of family life. This new family pattern will emerge slowly, a little at a time. Perhaps you now go to church on Saturday night because everyone wants to sleep in on Sunday morning. You may do major shopping only twice a month on paydays, and each child may be in charge of his or her own laundry. This new routine works well and you all feel good about it.

Your family has adapted to the changes. The losses still exist—but they are being faced and slowly mourned. During the period of transition to this new family system perhaps all family members utilized some different coping techniques. Eventually, however, you become a functioning single-parent family with teenage children. This is not the family dreamed of—but it is your family and you are making it work.

If you have just separated, then the process of mourning, coping, and adapting is just beginning. Have patience with yourself and your children. Reading this book, thinking about each topic, doing some of the exercises may help.

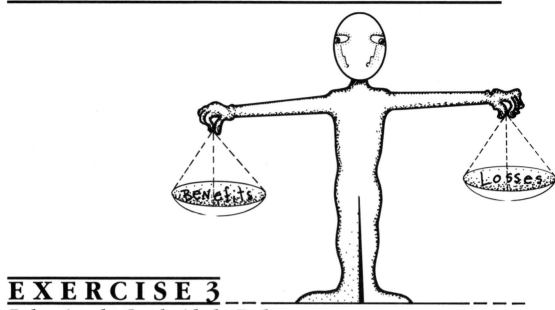

EXERCISE 3
Balancing the Good with the Bad

FOR YOU

Take out a large piece of paper. At the top, write the words "Changes" and "How to Adapt." Then list the name of each person in the family (including your former spouse) down the left side. Cite what you believe are the major changes for each family member, and next to the changes write any suggestion you might have to help the person adapt to the negative or positive developments caused by the divorce.

EXAMPLE

	Changes	**How to Adapt**
Joe (me) **(schoolteacher)**	1. Loss of dream. I wanted "perfect" family.	1. Look at old pictures of family. Think about what a "perfect" family is.
	2. Lower self-esteem. Is there something wrong with me?	2. Enroll in the divorce support group at church.
	3. Miss caring relationships. I miss daily interaction with the kids.	3. Call the children more. Have them sleep over during the week.
	4. More time to do the things I want.	4. Take some post-masters courses. Don't feel guilty about moving on in life.

Maria **(former wife)**	1. Miss caring relationships. She probably misses my parents—and even me. 2. Less money and time. A teacher's salary isn't much to begin with. She will have to work full time. 3. New friends and social life.	1. Suggest my parents keep in touch with Maria. 2. Discuss the possibility of using some of the cash value of our life insurance to help her stay in the home at least one more year. 3. Try not to resent her rebuilding her life. (This may be hard—especially if she starts to date.)
Joe, Jr. (16)	1. Lower self-esteem. He has only one friend whose parents are divorced. 2. Loss of home. He has lived in the same house and neighborhood since he was five. He has many friends here. 3. Visits with Dad are scheduled and planned.	1. Talk with him about divorce in general. Try to make it not such a taboo subject. 2. Same as Maria's #2. 3. Enjoy our time together.
Jason (14)	1. Very upset by the breakup of his family. 2. Loss of home. Same as Joe, Jr.'s, #2. 3. Same as Joe, Jr.'s, #3.	1. Talk with him about how he can have two families: one with me and one with Maria. 2. Same as Maria's #2. 3. Same as Joe, Jr.'s, #3.
Linda (8)	1. Loss of caring relationship. She and I are very close. 2. Loss of self-esteem. I don't know why. 3. Less tension between her parents.	1. Give Linda some special attention. Take her to her dance lessons. 2. Tell her the divorce wasn't her fault. 3. Encourage her to talk about how she feels now that Mommy and Daddy don't fight anymore.

Comment

Doing this exercise helped Joe see that selling the family home at this time would be especially stressful for Joe, Jr., and Jason—as well as his former wife. Although he wanted his half of the equity in the home, he realized that if Maria and the children could stay in the home longer it would allow them more time to adjust to the divorce. Joe decided to meet with Maria to try and work out a mutually agreed plan that would permit her to stay in the home longer. He also decided to be a little more involved with his children, including having specific focused discussions related to the divorce with each child. (Fortunately, Joe lives in the same town as Maria and can see the children frequently.)

Joe also realized that not all the changes brought about by the divorce were bad. He had more time to pursue the courses that would help him in his profession as a schoolteacher (and would also provide him with a raise). He also realized that especially for his eight-year-old daughter, Linda, the removal of the tension between himself and his former wife was having a positive effect.

Finally, Joe decided to enroll in a divorce support group. He hated to take this step because it openly signified the end of his marriage. He realized, however, that doing so might help him begin to feel better about himself.

EXERCISE FOR AGES 12-14

Pick out several family pictures from the past. Ask your child if he or she would like one framed to keep in his or her own room. As your young teenager looks through the pictures, the two of you may reminisce a little. This process will help your child mourn the family.

Another day, go shopping together for a frame for the picture. If your child hates to shop, pick up a frame yourself. Then place the family picture in the frame together.

EXERCISE FOR AGES 15-18

Older adolescents sometimes like personal letters, drawings, or poetry. Select one of the changes you listed for your child and then produce a letter, drawing, or poem expressing your understanding of this concern and what you propose to do about it. Put the message on your teen's pillow. Perhaps he or she will communicate in a similar manner. If not, you have reached out to your son or daughter in a creative and expressive way.

Dear Joe,

I know moving from the house and neighborhood would be very hard for you. I am going to try to work out a plan with your mother so you can stay in the house—at least until you graduate from high school.

If the plan doesn't work out, I want to you know that Mom and I have tried and that we're sorry the divorce is causing you these problems.

I love you.
Dad

TABLE TOPICS

1. What will each person miss most about the intact family?
2. Does anyone know a divorced family that seems to have adjusted very well? How did they do it?
3. Are there any positive things that have come from the changes in the family? What are they, or how can we think of some?

CHAPTER 4

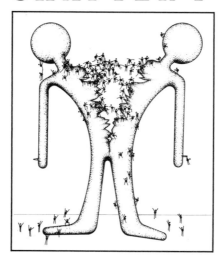

THE ADOLESCENT NEED
TO SEPARATE

"I hate Thanksgiving. You are supposed to just sit around with your family. It's so boring. I really want to be with my friends."

Janice, a 16-year-old

As every parent of teenagers quickly discovers, there is a variety of developmental stages adolescents go through—sometimes at breathtaking speed! This is a normal and healthy response necessary to prepare a child to become an adult.

Teenagers often exhibit a variety of behavior patterns that may drive parents crazy: talking incessantly on the telephone, playing loud music, talking back to elders, refusing to take school seriously. Some of these behaviors might indicate personal problems, but often they are a perfectly ordinary reaction to becoming one's own person. Negative actions and attitudes of adolescent children may be related to a parental divorce, or they may be merely part of the natural process of trying out new ideas. It is important for you to be able to tell the difference.

Janice was honest about how she felt about the upcoming Thanksgiving holiday—she wanted no part of it. At first her mother, Betty, thought that the reason her daughter wanted to be with her friends was that Janice's parents had divorced two years previously and at holiday time Janice was reminded of how the family was no longer together. After Betty talked with several other parents of teenagers, however, she discovered other adolescent children—from both divorced and "traditional" families—expressed the same desire. "Please let me be with my friends on Thanksgiving!" "If I go to Grandma's, may I leave after we have finished eating?"

Many teens feel strongly about spending time with their friends. Some parents seemed bewildered or hurt. "Are we so awful that spending one day with us will kill you?" "I thought we were a close family—what is going on?"

Betty had been raised in a very traditional, patriarchal family, where children (even growing adolescents) were never allowed to voice opinions or express feelings. She was trying to create a different atmosphere for her children and wanted to understand them and keep communications open. Betty found talking with other parents was one way to help discover what was "normal" or "average." She didn't always agree with the rules of other families, but it certainly helped to have more information before she made her own parenting decisions.

After considering Janice's desire to be with friends on Thanksgiving, Betty decided to try a compromise. She allowed Janice to spend the Wednesday evening prior to Thanksgiving with her best friend. Janice ate an early Thanksgiving dinner at her friend's home and, in the late afternoon, joined her family at her grandmother's. Everyone was satisfied, but best of all Janice and Betty had deflected a potential conflict into a closer mutual understanding.

Betty's experience is probably one you will go through many times as you raise your teenager. Remember that *all* parents must do the same. Adding the dimension of parental divorce to understanding your adolescent will simply complicate this process. Betty had almost decided that Janice's reaction to being with her extended family on a holiday was related to her parents' divorce. This caused Betty to begin to get "re-angry" at her former husband for placing their children in this position. Yet after she checked around with other parents she discovered that Janice's desire to spend time with friends appeared to have very little to do with the divorce.

As you parent your children you need to keep in mind that parental divorce is a major event in their lives and that the divorce will influence and affect them in numerous ways. The divorce, however, is only one factor in their development.

SEPARATION

An important and perhaps most painful developmental process in adolescence is the need for separation. This healthy and normal reaction is compounded when it is done in the context of another separation—that of the child's parents.

In this context, even the word *separation* immediately triggers so many negative images and feelings. Yet to become a healthy, functioning adult your child will eventually need to be able to function autonomously from his or her family of origin. This does not mean your child will toss you out, never spend time with you, not care for you and other family members. It does not mean your child must move across the country and never see you again. What it does mean is that your child, as an adult, must be able to make adult decisions and adult commitments, and that he or she is able to make decisions and commitments based upon feeling comfortable, confident, and competent in his or her adult self. This can only happen by psychologically, socially, economically separating from parents.

Separation is a difficult process that often begins when a child is in junior high. Everyone knows most teenagers hang out together—they want to dress alike, talk alike, like the same movies, the same music, and have the same cultural heroes (isn't it interesting that the hero or heroine is often the complete opposite of the families' life style and values—e.g., Eddie Murphy, Madonna, Sylvester Stallone). Within every teen group there exists a strict conformity rule—even if the youngsters believe they are total non-conformists.

In junior high, teens usually develop an awareness of "in" groups and the need to be accepted by their chosen group. It now becomes more important for them to be accepted by peers than by parents or teachers. If you forbid your seventh- or eighth-grade daughter to wear makeup, for example, don't be surprised or hurt if you find she keeps makeup in her locker at school and puts it on immediately upon entering school. Other examples of conformity are wanting to wear exclusive brand name clothes or—just the opposite—dressing in tattered old clothes or insisting on outrageous haircuts that may embarrass and enrage parents. If you and your child have been caught in the dress, hair, or makeup struggle, then you know the separation process is under way.

Another area in which adolescents begin to separate from family is in the questioning of moral and religious values. Many youth, for example, announce that they no longer believe in the teachings of their religion. Your child may be quite outspoken about how stupid he or she thinks your church or synagogue is, and may even state he or she no longer believes in God. This does not mean faith is lost forever. It only means your child is going through a time in life where many things are questioned—especially parental values and beliefs. Your child wants to feel grownup, older, and separate. "Look at me—I can function and think very well without my parents. In fact I think my parents are sort of dumb!" Many questioning adolescents return to their families' faith (and other values) when they themselves become parents.

Music preference is another source of great conflict between adults and teenagers. It often seems that adolescents like a particular music exactly because it causes their parents such chagrin. One useful exercise for parents is to remember back to when they were teenagers and to remember what their parents thought of the popular teen music of the time.

Family rules can also be an especially difficult issue. Many teenagers seem to spend an inordinate amount of time figuring out how to bend or stretch the rules beyond recognition or even to delight in breaking them whenever they think they can get away with it. It is important at this time for parents to reevaluate their family rules and to decide which are critical for the health and safety of the teenager and the family and which are merely preferences for the orderly running of a household. Enforcement should then be carried out accordingly.

DIVORCE AND THE SEPARATING ADOLESCENT

All families experience some problems as their adolescent begins the separation process. There are a few special pitfalls, however, of which the divorced parent needs to be aware. Divorced parents may find themselves lonely, sad, and in need of help in maintaining the home. During the crisis period when parents are separating—and the family is forming two new homes—many adults find themselves unable to function and cope as they had when the family was together. The parent may turn to a teenage child to fill in the gaps for the parent.

Alfred doesn't go to the football game because his dad is going to be alone on Friday night. Ruth stays home from school, pretending to be sick, because she knows her depressed mother feels better when someone is in the home. Fifteen-year-old Kara's mother asks her for advice on how to look for a job. Steven's father makes it clear that they will have to sell the family home if Steven doesn't mow the lawn and paint the living room. These are very heavy demands—emotionally and physically—to place on a teenager who is not only going through the normal separation process of adolescence but is also experiencing the many changes associated with a divorce.

Of course it is important for all children to contribute to the welfare of the family—having jobs and helping out at home promotes the development of responsibility. When the child is expected, however, to assume the adult role—caring for the parent as if the parent were the child—then the child is not allowed to separate appropriately from the family. If you think that inadvertently you have used your child as an adult—as a substitute spouse or parent—then it would be a good idea to consult with a counselor who can help you in developing other ways of getting the support you need and allowing your child be a teenager.

Another pitfall that some divorced parents fall into is connecting all separation-type behaviors with the former spouse. For example, if John comes home with alcohol on his breath it is "because your father never demonstrated any decent values," or if Suzanne wants designer jeans it is "your mother always had to have the best." This type of response is doing two things. First, it undermines the child's developing sense of independent thought: "You mean I'm not capable of deciding what type of jeans I like? Don't I have a brain?" It also strengthens the child's attachment/identification with the criticized parent: "I like drinking beer (or buying designer jeans), so I guess I really am like Dad (or Mom). No wonder they divorced. I would divorce her (or him) too." The very thing the parent didn't want to happen—having the child identifying with some aspect of the other parent—has been strengthened.

It is important to learn to speak from a position of how you yourself feel about a problem and not try to blame the behavior on your former spouse. "I will not tolerate you drinking. I realize most kids will try alcohol at some point, but for many reasons—legal and health—this is not acceptable in our home. Perhaps tomorrow we can sit down and discuss what happened tonight, and I will need to have you guarantee me that I can trust you not to drink again." This parent was upset about her child's behavior and was very clear about the family values—no drinking. The parent did not belittle or humiliate the teenager, however, and was careful not link the separating behavior with the former spouse.

Approaching problems with your teen in this manner does not mean that your former spouse may not have some negative personality traits. After all, you are divorced and he or she probably possesses some traits you do not admire. Do not mix these concerns or feelings with parent/child issues.

YOUR OWN SEPARATION CONCERNS

Many adults reach adulthood, marry, and have families, yet never fully separate from their families of origin. A man may take over his father's business not because he is especially interested in the work but because it is expected of him. A woman may clean house or cook in a certain manner because she fears disappointing her mother. Adults who have successfully separated from their parents may go into a family business or prepare some of the same home cooked meals as they had growing up, but the motivation for these behaviors differs from that of the non-separated adult. The separated adult makes decisions based on a free choice of alternatives—not based on fear, guilt, or humiliation.

For some adults, their own divorce becomes a life event that finally forces a separation from their own parents. There are many people who do not approve of divorce. In some instances this non-approval is expressed as anger and hostility toward their own adult child.

Connie's husband Art was somewhat lazy. He had a job, but after work preferred to plop in front of the T.V. until bedtime. Art's "laid-back" attitude carried over to other areas of family life. For example, he let Connie make most decisions related to money and the children. Connie was basically an energetic person with many ideas for family vacations, fun weekends, redecorating, etc. After fourteen years of trying to motivate her husband, however, Connie decided to get a divorce. Connie's parents lived only two blocks away and had always been quite involved with Connie, Art, and the children. They did not approve of their daughter getting a divorce. "After all," her mother reasoned, "Art is a good provider and doesn't run around and drink." When month after month Connie stood fast by her decision to divorce, her parents, especially her mother, became very angry. Basically Connie's mother was saying "You must do what I say or I won't be nice to you. You must agree with me." Connie divorced anyway, and two years later she still has no contact with her parents. Holidays are painful reminders of not one, but two, broken families.

When Connie—at the age of thirty-four—had ideas that differed from those of her parents, it became clear that this adult child/parent relationship could not tolerate differences. Connie continues to explore her relationship with her parents in counseling and is hopeful that in the future she will be able to reestablish contact with them. She feels good, however, about making her own decision and finally separating from her parents. Her own experience has been helpful to her in coping with some of the separation reactions of her own two teenage daughters.

There are other areas and reactions of parents to their adult child's divorce that may reawaken some unresolved parent/child concerns: How soon and whom to date? Where to work? How to spend money? Where to live? These are areas where conflicts may arise.

If you find yourself in conflict with your parents concerning some aspects of your new life, you too are experiencing some separation concerns. It is best to handle these concerns in a very direct but non-hostile manner. Tell your parents how you feel and how you would like for them to respond. For example, "Mother, I know you and Father don't like it that I am dating before the divorce is final. Today many people date before the divorce is finalized and I need to have some fun. My new friend is a very thoughtful, considerate person. We only go out when the children are visiting with their mother (or father), so please don't think I'm a bad or immoral person. I really love you both and need you to support me—especially during this stressful time."

There is no guarantee that this open, direct approach will work, but in most cases it does. Very few parents refuse to support their children when they are asked for specific help. In any case, this approach will help you deal with your own adolescent child's need to separate from you and become his or her own person.

HELP FOR YOU

Both divorce and the teenage years are stressful, trying times for parents and their children. If you are a single parent trying to make all of the parenting decisions alone, it may be even more stressful—for most parents really need to talk with another interested adult about the conflicts they are experiencing with their child. In two-parent families, Mom and Dad can huddle behind closed doors and discuss what to do about Jimmy wanting to quit piano lessons, or Tammy refusing to go to Sunday school. The strategy devised by two concerned parents may not be perfect, but at least each parent feels listened to and supported.

If you are facing the teen separation period alone, where can you turn for support?

1. Your Former Spouse.

If you have established a cooperative post-divorce "co-parenting" relationship with your former spouse, then your child's other parent is a very logical source of support. If you want to consult with your former spouse about your teen it would be best to meet on a neutral ground—such as a local coffeeshop or a quiet, private office or waiting room. Meeting in either parent's home may give your children the message that one way of getting the parents back together is to create crisis. (It is very revealing that many auto accidents, failing grades, and teen pregnancies occur when parents separate. One by-products of these crises is that the parents are forced to talk together—a result not totally lost on confused teenagers.)

Keep your discussions with your former spouse focused on your concerns for your children. "I'm upset about Frankie wanting to wear an earring. What approach do you think we should take? I don't want to be old-fashioned, but I'm not certain his wearing earrings is something I can accept. How do you feel about it? What do you think we should do?"

Notice that in this illustration Frankie's father was asking his former wife for her ideas. He was not asking her to solve the dilemma, punish the child, or be the heavy. He also was not blaming her or the divorce for this problem.

Frankie's father may or may not agree with his former wife's suggestions, but he knows she really loves their son and wants the best for him.

On the other hand, if you find yourself wanting to call your former spouse quite frequently then perhaps you are using "parenting concerns" as a way to keep contact with him or her. Learn to make many parenting decisions on your own, reserving consultations for very troubling issues.

Some divorced parents do not have cordial, or even civil, relationships following the divorce. Others do not respect their former spouse's ideas about child rearing. These are not ideal situations for parents or their children, but divorced couples often cannot have the ideal. If you find yourself unable or unwilling to use your former spouse as a parenting resource, there are other people who may be helpful.

2. Extended Family Members.

Your parents or grown brothers and sisters may be good listening posts if you are facing separation-related conflicts with your child. Grandparents have already raised children, and sometimes they are wise and patient. Aunts and uncles are usually interested and care about their nieces' and nephews' development.

A word of warning before turning to your parents for parenting support, however. Grandparents were making decisions about their teenagers more than twenty-five years ago. Culturally accepted adolescent behavior (clothing style, music, interests) has dramatically changed in a quarter of a century. Ponder what it was like for your mother or father when they were adolescents. So if you ask your parents for ideas related to decisions about your teen, be prepared to learn that they may not understand your child and may have very different ideas about stances to take: "No child of mine would ever wear an earring!"

If your parents (or your siblings) generally do not seem to understand teens, then perhaps it would be better to get support from others. Then you could calmly inform them of your decisions *after* they have been made. "I have decided to let Frankie get his ear pierced to wear an earring. I know it may seem weird to you; it certainly seems weird to me too. But many of the boys in his high school—especially in his group—are wearing earrings. To kids today it doesn't mean a boy is effeminate or anything—to them it's sort of 'cool.' After thinking about it, I have decided I am not going to make a big deal out of it."

Your relatives may not agree with your decisions, but they will see that you are now a grown-up parent yourself and will respect your decisions for your children.

3.   Friends and Other Parents.

A good source of information and support for parents is the parents of other adolescents in your community. Your child has friends, and it is beneficial in many ways for you to know their parents. Of course, it is almost impossible to know all the parents well. Most parents of teenagers are very busy—many of them are working, trying to keep up with running a home, and raising a family. However, when your child is visiting a friend you may need to call to clarify arrangements. At that time introduce yourself to the parent and chat a minute. Let other parents know you are available and interested in child-related concerns. Then if you become concerned about some behavior or other problem you can call one of the parents and ask if he or she would be willing to talk with you about your concerns. This is not to say that you should make your decisions based on what other parents do, but it is an important bit of information to check out. This is exactly what Janice's mother did when she was trying to make a decision about Thanksgiving.

In the group of adult friends you know at work, at church, or in other social contexts, there may be one or two people who seem to really understand and like adolescents. This person may be an excellent resource to use if you have concerns about your child. As with your former spouse, ask specifically for the type of help you want: "When are most kids allowed to date? Kate, who is fifteen, was asked to the homecoming dance and wants to stay out all night. Since she's my first one in high school I'm not sure what to do."

You may not want your friend to give you any advice at all. Perhaps you just want someone to listen to you. "I need a good listener who can identify with how hard it is to raise a child—do you have time? Have I been through a weekend! Frankie wanted to get his ear pierced. . . ."

In both of these illustrations, the parent clearly communicated with the friend what he or she wanted—advice, opinion, or a good listener. If you need a listener and get an advice giver ("you should have" or "I would have"), you may begin to feel frustrated or angry with your friend and would be better served seeking help elsewhere.

4.   Professionals Who Work with Adolescents.

Teachers, guidance counselors, social workers, psychologists, rabbis, ministers, and religious group leaders in your community are potentially helpful parental supports. Many communities offer different types of parent groups—such as "Parent Effectiveness Training" and "Tough Love." In addition to these standardized approaches to parenting, there may be topic-related parent groups ("How to Be a Single Parent," "How to Know If Your Child Is Abusing Drugs," etc.) offered at schools, churches, or synagogues or in other community settings.

Participating in one of these parent groups may be very helpful. You will learn some new things about parenting an adolescent and you may make some new adult friends who care about their children.

Regardless of whom you draw upon for support, however, remember that you are ultimately your child's parent. Get information, ideas, and suggestions. Then take time to think: What do you really feel is the best thing to do? Why? If you were your child, how would you like to be treated? Bringing the focus back to yourself will help you accept the responsibility for your parenting decisions and actions.

EXERCISE 4
Separation Preparation

FOR YOU

List the name of each of your adolescent children along the side of a piece of paper. At the top of the page write: "Separating Behaviors," "How I Feel," and "What to Do?" Then think about each adolescent child and fill in any behavior you see that might indicate your child is becoming a separate person. Next reflect on how this behavior makes you feel. Finally decide if there anything you could do to help you and your child remain close to the family while at the same time developing confidence in his or her own ideas and talents.

EXAMPLE

	Separating Behavior	How I Feel	What to Do
Anne 14	Watches MTV incessantly	Angry—I hate the sex and violence	Tell Anne why I don't like the station.
			Ask her to limit her time watching the channel.
			Admit to myself that she will continue to watch it when I'm not home or she's at a friend's house.
			Reexamine what I object to. Perhaps talking to my younger sister Renee (who also watches) MTV will help me understand why Anne is attracted to it.
Sammy 18	Is "going with" Erin and spending too much time at her house.	Worried. Are they too serious. Could they be having sex?	Talk with Sammy about his feelings toward Erin. Does he think he is in love?
		Jealous. If I'm honest I'd admit I wish I had someone who treated me as Sammy treats Erin.	Talk frankly with him about responsible sexual behavior.
			Encourage the two of them to do some things with Anne and me.
			Remember how it was to be young and in love.

Comment

After completing the exercise, Barbara, mother of Anne and Sammy, discovered that if she were going to remain close to her children during adolescence she was going to need to be very clear about her own values and beliefs. She also realized there were many things that Anne and Sammy could do that were beyond her control: she could not keep them glued to her side day and night, she could not control their brains. Thus, although she strongly disapproved of both music videos and pre-marital sex, she realized that Sammy and Erin might at some point choose different values. Therefore she felt it important to be honest about her own values, but not to expect Sammy automatically to have the same values. Barbara hoped Sammy would talk with his father about male/female relations, but she decided that as the custodial parent she must take responsibility for creating an ongoing open dialogue with Sammy about relationships and responsibility for one's actions. The sexual aspect of this discussion made her nervous, but Barbara was determined to try.

EXERCISE FOR AGES 12-14

Take magazines and cut out pictures of several areas where you perceive you and your teen are experiencing conflicting views (for example, a package of cigarettes, a "punk" hairdo, a church or synagogue). At dinnertime place one picture on your plate and one on your child's plate. Tell your child that

65

you think that there may be conflict building up around these areas and that this game will help you understand each other. Each of you will tell the other person how he or she feels about the topic pictured on the plate. The other person is allowed only to listen. Set a time limit of 5 minutes. After the first person has expressed his or her views, the listener tells what he or she has heard.

Next, the positions are reversed. The second person shares opinions about the topic on his or her plate and the other person must listen. The same procedure is followed: 5 minutes of ideas, listening, and repeating what the speaker said.

Now comes the hard part! Exchange pictures and repeat the process. After each person has expressed opinions on each topic the game is over. No one is to continue trying to change the other person's mind. The purpose is to communicate openly—to get to know each other, not to control each other. (This game can be repeated occasionally and can be done with more than one teenager at a time. Do not include younger, pre-adolescent children in this game, however, for it may limit or stifle honest discussion.)

EXERCISES FOR AGES 15-18

Go with your older teen to buy a tape or record. Let him or her tell you about the performer or group. Later listen to the album together. Share your honest reactions with your child without putting down your child's likes or dislikes. (Note: You do not need to like teen music. This exercise is designed to facilitate understanding.)

Now reverse the process. Dig out an old record that you liked when you were a teenager. (Go out and buy it in an "oldies" store if you must.) Tell your child about the performer or group and then listen to the album together. Let your teen share his or her reaction to your music. (You might even want to share how your parents reacted to this music when you were a child.)

TABLE TOPICS

1. What does each person hope to do after high school: job (what kind), college (what major)?
2. Why do people of different generations like different kinds of music, movies, clothes, etc.?
3. How has the divorce affected everyone's feelings of being in control of his or her own destiny?

CHAPTER 5

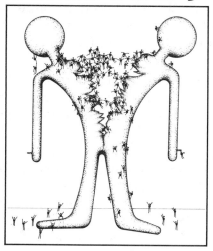

ADOLESCENT IDENTITY FORMATION

"Now that my parents are getting divorced, will I be like one of those losers from a divorced home?"

Tony, a fourteen-year-old

No issue is more critical to a teenager than that of identity formation. Some would say that the major "work" of adolescence is to develop a strong sense of who one really is as an individual. This is a difficult task for all teens, and it can be severely compounded by a parental divorce.

Tony's question illustrates how divorce can affect a teenager. A person obviously does not automatically turn into a "loser" because his or her parents divorce, yet Tony firmly held many beliefs about the children of divorced parents that were basically myths. By thinking about divorce only in terms of how other people perceived him, Tony was avoiding feeling his own pain and confusion resulting from his parents' divorce.

Despite the fact that today's teenagers grow up in a culture inundated by divorce, many still hold negative, judgmental views of people living in post-divorce families. If their own families experience divorce, adolescents can turn these negative attitudes toward themselves: "I am bad because I am from a divorced family." If a youth really believes he or she is bad, then the behavior that follows may in fact become destructive or "bad."

Tony is fourteen, an adolescent. He is trying to pull together a sense of who he is, to consolidate his identity. This is a long process, and many teens experiment with a variety of identities before all the pieces that make up a solid adult identity come together for them.

Identity formation is much more than just preparing for one's occupation or career. Think of the adjectives you would use to describe yourself. It might be: white (race), female (gender), heterosexual (sexual preference), daughter/mother/wife (family roles), Methodist (religion), secretary (profession), Southerner (family roots), Central High (school loyalty). These might describe you well, but there are even more parts—more aspects that make up your identity.

When one is a teenager, one begins to explore or think about these various aspects of the self. What is it really like to be white (or black or brown or yellow or red)? Do I really believe in God? Do I want to attend church? I really like music—could I ever make it in a band? What kind of other jobs are available in the entertainment field? Could I make enough money to live on? Do I really want to pursue music and not pursue my interest and talent in carpentry? Can I pursue both? How? If I do become a musician, will other people think I'm strange? Can I get married and be a musician? Maybe I should get a carpenter job and just do music as a hobby? Perhaps I should go to college and investigate other talents I might have. And on and on.

These are very important questions to teenagers. They are beginning to explore and pull together for themselves identities that will last them a lifetime.

DIFFUSED IDENTITY

For some people, their identity remains hazy throughout their lives. A fifty-year-old might still be asking "What do I want to be when I grow up?" Adults who have diffused identities have been traveling through life feeling attached only to part of themselves. Perhaps a man likes being a father and a home-owner, but dislikes his work. He has not really "found" himself—except in a negative way. "I know what I'm not and what I don't like, but I don't know what I am and what I do like." This lack of feeling centered, of not knowing who one is, is referred to as "role confusion." The possibility of living with role confusion is terrifying to most teenagers.

Another problem encountered in identity formation occurs when an adolescent forms a "premature" identity. At the age of ten a youngster says, "I am going to be a lawyer when I grow up." Everything the child, youth, and finally young adult does leads toward becoming an attorney: good grades, the right college, acceptance at law school, focused study, and finally the goal—passing the bar exam. After working in a law firm for three years, the young lawyer feels depressed. She finds herself listening to jazz records wishing she had continued clarinet lessons and finally experiencing the musical part of herself beginning to emerge. Now "the lawyer"—an identity defined at ten years of age—shatters, and the young adult begins looking at multiple interests and choices—a process in which many of her friends were engaged in high school and college. At that time everyone had thought that this girl had her life focused and "together." Now she realizes that perhaps it had been a mistake to select such a major component of her adult identity at ten years of age.

The process known as identity formation is complicated and personalized. It is also a process that takes place over time and does not usually consolidate until one is in the mid to late twenties. But the teen years are when the process really begins. What happens during that time will influence a person throughout life.

All the life experiences an adolescent has will influence the identity formation process. If you have provided your child with a religious education, discussed your political orientation, played music in the home, coached your youngster's soccer team, etc., then—as the adult identity forms—these experiences will be important factors in helping establish his or her identity.

FAMILY IDENTITY

One very important aspect of a person's identity is derived from identification with the family of origin. "We are the Johnsons," said with pride, may connote to a Johnson family member an understanding that Johnsons are hard-working, clean, and punctual. Or "You know how the Wilson women are," said with a smile when ten-year-old Melanie Wilson comes home from school with a black eye. To the Wilsons it is important to defend one's point of view and exhibiting a hot temper is acceptable—especially for the females. Many families have qualities that they feel are "them," and it is the composite of these qualities that constitute a family identity.

One aspect of family identity that many families embrace is "We are a happy (or sort of happy), intact, nuclear family. We can work out our problems. We are a respectable, normal family." This statement is usually not spoken out loud, but when a family member begins describing family beliefs and values this family motto often emerges. Holding this self image can provide a family with strength in times of stress and enhance individual family members' sense of self-esteem. If parental divorce intrudes on this family, however, the family identity—happy, intact, problem-solving, normal—may be severely strained or shattered.

After a divorce, family members may begin to question the goodness of their own family. "If my parents get divorced, are we still normal?" "Will others see us as bad?" "Is everyone looking at us saying 'I know Mr. and Mrs. Conrad are divorced'?" These thoughts and questions are typical responses of adolescents, although you too may be going through a process of wondering if your family is still really an acceptable family and how others view you.

It is important to discuss these potential concerns with your teenager, but before you discuss them, take time to sort through your own feelings toward your current family structure. A single-parent family—a post-divorce family—can be happy, can solve problems, and can care for each other. The only family dimension that all divorces change is being an *intact*—mother, father, and children living together—family. The children still have two parents, although the parents are no longer married and no longer live together. In most instances, children are part of two family constellations: the mother/children family and father/children family. Thus your children will need to adjust their identity to include "Mom's family" and "Dad's family."

LOST IDENTITY

In the years preceding the divorce, your family developed a unique and interesting history. It began when you and your former spouse met and were courting. It continued to build, marked by important events such as your graduations from school, wedding, setting up a household, the birth of children, and perhaps the purchase of a home and a move to a different community.

Over time you developed important family rituals and ways to celebrate. Birthdays, Christmas or Hanukkah, Thanksgiving, and Easter or Passover are holidays that your family probably celebrated in special ways. These are memories you all—including your children's other parent—share. You may remember such events with fondness, and it may make you feel sad or angry that they will not be able to be celebrated by the same people in the same way ever again. Your teens will have their own feelings—which may or may not mirror yours.

There are also everyday rituals that your pre-divorce family shared that may now have to change. Perhaps your family always went out for pizza on Friday night, roasted corn on hot summer days, cheered the school ball team together, and went grocery shopping every Thursday night. Although these events may not seem as important as special holidays, they give a family its own identity and helps teenagers form theirs.

Family identity is more than individual family rituals and routines, however. It includes the certainty that each member is attached to the same family roots. These roots include an attachment to family names, family history and folklore, and perhaps even a family hometown. People, and especially young people, want to feel proud of their family roots.

When a divorce takes place, there is often a ripping apart of attachments made to the "other half" of the family identity or roots. Both parents and children are suddenly cut off from seeing people, such as cousins and aunts, who prior to the divorce had played important roles in their lives. (This is often more difficult for teenagers than for younger children because they have had more time to develop these relationships.) Some children even lose the name-connection to their mother if she resumes her maiden name after the divorce. Understanding that you and your children have suffered a major blow to family and personal identity is a major step in beginning to rebuild and solidify a sense of pride and identity in the post-divorce family.

CHANGING ROUTINES

One's identity—as a person and as a family member—is expressed in many ways. How we carry out our daily routines is important in proclaiming our identity to the world. As special events and holidays arise, you and your children must decide if you will continue doing things as you have in the past or will change your family rituals. Maybe you went shopping on Thursday nights because that was the day your former spouse was paid, but now you receive your child support check at the first of the month and are paid on the 15th and 30th of the month. It may be easier to shop on Friday nights or Sunday afternoons, so you change that routine.

The family may have gone out for pizza on Friday because everyone was tired from the week and wanted to celebrate in a small way the start of the weekend. You might still want to celebrate making it through the week, but you might no longer have your children with you every weekend. Perhaps you could make another evening during the week a "special night" for you and your children. When your children are away, make plans to do something different for yourself. Go to a shopping center and take time to look through a new bookstore, go bowling, visit a friend, or buy yourself a frozen dinner and watch T.V. in bed. Try to recognize when a change of family routines is going to be painful and plan and build new, helpful routines for yourself and your children.

In the first years following the separation, each special event or season will bring up memories of what the family was doing at that time the previous year. Some of these memories may be bittersweet because at the time the event was pleasant and now things have changed so dramatically. In the spring you recall how cute your sixteen-year-old son looked as a child out in the backyard learning to throw a baseball with his dad, your former husband. Or your daughter gives you a look while you are bowling that reminds you of the way your former wife used to look at you when you were on a team together. These same experiences are happening all the time to your children—especially if they are teenaged.

Other memories may not be very pleasant. You recall how you had to fill the children's Christmas stockings alone because your husband had drunk six glasses of wine and had passed out on the couch; or you remember taking the children to church alone on Easter because your wife "just had to play golf." Teens also have memories that make them feel sad and lonely. Both you and your children need time to mourn the loss of the pre-divorce family. It is very important for you to allow your child the opportunity to do this mourning. Your child may say "Dad, remember how funny it was when Mom spilled the spaghetti sauce on Grandma?" This is an indication that your child is reviewing in his or her mind some aspect of your family life before the divorce. If you react to these comments in a negative way, such as "That was a long time ago and I don't want to talk about it," or "Yes, your mom certainly was clumsy," then you are communicating that conversation about the pre-divorce family is unwelcome.

We mourn by remembering and reminiscing. It is part of how we decide who we are and what we are like. In the first year or two after the separation, expect your child to want to talk about things as they "used to be." Over time this type of reminiscing will diminish. You and your children will have developed a new family style that includes aspects of the pre-divorce family but also includes new rituals and routines. Your former spouse will hopefully have done the same.

PARENTS' ATTITUDES TOWARD DIVORCE

If you want to help your teenager develop a positive attitude about himself or herself, you need to show by your own words and actions that your new family is a real family! Reflecting on your own attitudes and feelings may help you understand what your adolescent child is going through.

Before you were divorced, you and your former spouse had attitudes toward divorce and toward children from divorced homes. These attitudes were expressed in subtle ways that now may be influencing how your child feels about being from a divorced family. If you felt divorce was an unfortunate event that was sad for all family members—but that the divorce did not automatically make people immoral, troubled, or bad—then your children have a similar attitude. On the other hand, if either or both of you felt uneasy about your child playing with a child from a single-parent family or remarked "Oh, isn't he (or she) the one whose parents are divorced?" when you heard of a teenager who got picked up for drunk driving, then your children probably have very negative feelings toward divorced families.

Mark was very agitated and angry when he found out that his parents, Melissa and Martin, were going to be divorced. He dissolved into tears—"Now I'm going to be like all those other children from divorced families." "How are they?" he was asked. "Oh, you know, they get poor grades and always drop out of school."

Melissa had a predominantly neutral attitude toward divorce, but Martin felt very much the way Mark did. The father believed that divorce would instantly turn anyone's child into a neurotic misfit. His attitude was transmitted almost completely to his son.

Parental divorce can be so stressful that a teenager may experience some, or even many, adjustment problems following parental separation. These adjustment problems are not, however, necessarily long lasting or forever debilitating. A divorce does not have to overshadow the longstanding strengths and resources the family has possessed.

If a child graduates with honors, is elected class president, or becomes a star basketball player, you never hear people say "This great accomplishment is because the parents are divorced." Yet if a child gets into trouble with the law, abuses drugs, or becomes pregnant before marriage, such behavior is often blamed on the parental divorce. The truth is that both types of children—the successful or the troubled teen—may come from either a divorced or an intact home. If you have transmitted negative feelings about divorce to your child, perhaps you could begin to neutralize some of these negative messages. Remember that it is important for children to feel good about their families, whether divorced or intact.

You might say something like this: "Before Mom and I were divorced I used to think that divorce was so awful that it would ruin everyone in the family. Now that we are divorced ourselves, I see that I was wrong. Divorce is certainly painful and confusing, but I still think we are good people and still have a nice family. I guess I really didn't know enough about divorce before this happened to us." This is a short, clear message, not filled with blame or shame. It can help your children feel more hopeful about their family and the future. Only say something like this to your child if you mean it, however, for if the words are hollow your children will sense it and feel even more uneasy and worried about the divorce.

The location of your home, community attitudes, the types of families you know, your former spouse's attitude, and your own attitude toward divorce in general will affect how your adolescent views divorce. Perhaps the factor that has the strongest effect on your child's attitude, however, is how you are feeling about what happened to your family and to you personally. Divorce often comes as a shock, and you may be left feeling disillusioned and frightened. Some parents become so angry and upset that these feelings take over their whole being.

There are women who complain, for example, "Why did he do this to me? I do not want to go out to work. I got married to stay home and raise children. That is the life we agreed to." There are men who say "How could she break the marriage promise? It was a commitment. It is unfair that I am losing my home and my children and I have no choice in the matter. My choice was to stay married!"

These are normal and understandable responses to an event—divorce—that was not anticipated and often not wanted by one of the parties. If you become stuck in one of these pessimistic, victimized, angry stances for too long, however, it will have a negative effect on you and most especially on your children. It may even become an element of your teenager's developing identity. If you dwell on the injustice of your divorce, people will begin to drift away from you. Even your children may pull back. As they and others stay away, you will feel even more angry and more victimized: "No one really cares that my life has been ruined." This vicious cycle will continue until you break it. If you cannot do it for yourself, do it for your children.

There may be aspects of your former spouse's personality and life style that you really don't like, for example. By constantly complaining, pointing out faults, and trying to resist your teenager's identifying with the other parent, however, you will be damaging your child and complicating his or her process of identity formation. Remember, your teen is currently questioning many aspects of life. He or she will probably examine and question aspects of the family life prior to the divorce and also look at you and your former spouse's family style. Now, through this process he or she will select aspects of the family pre- and post-divorce that will be incorporated into his or her identity. Therefore, it is important that your adolescent does not get the message that living in a divorced family is bad, or that divorced family members are bad people, or that being divorced is something of which to be ashamed.

Parental divorce is sad; divorce usually causes all family members pain and disillusionment. The fact that parents divorce, however, does not mean there is anything wrong with the family or the individuals in the family. Divorce is a legal procedure that results when parents cannot or do not want to stay married to each other. If you and your children can understand and accept the divorce as part of your life, you will be well on the road to accepting your current family and your teenagers will have a better chance of constructing a positive self-image and identity.

PARENT PERCEPTION

Another equally significant contribution to adolescents' self-esteem is how they perceive both parents. All people adopt some qualities of their parents. The parental qualities the adolescent chooses to incorporate into his or her adult identity are qualities that he or she feel will be helpful in living a happy, productive adult life. Since no parent—divorced or not—has "perfect" qualities (whatever "perfect" qualities are), children end up with an identity that is a compilation of a variety of attributes of their parents and other role models. Thus, you are certainly not the only influence on your child's development. Nor is the developing child a passive victim—developing an identity exactly as his or her parents wish or identifying with the less desirable parental qualities while remaining immune to positive traits. The adolescent has an active—indeed the preeminent—role in determining his or her identity.

Your adolescent will carefully scrutinize what you and your former spouse do and say and will screen this information—selecting, rejecting, reviewing, thinking: "Whom do I admire?" "Why?" "Mom says Dad is unfair. Has he been unfair to me?" "Dad says I'm just like Mom; am I? Is that good or bad?" Through this process of thinking about you and your former spouse, your adolescent will select qualities about each of you to keep for himself or herself.

It is very important for you not to denigrate the other parent; yet it is also very important for you to be honest with your teenager. If you openly criticize the other parent, you will in fact be criticizing part of your child, and your child may strongly identify with the very quality you so hate. If you are dishonest about your feelings toward your former spouse, your teenager will eventually find out and learn that you are not to be trusted!

Jack's wife was vivacious and fun-loving, which was one factor that contributed to her becoming involved with some other men. Jack labeled this behavior "immoral," "whorish," "bad." His adolescent son, Dan, enjoyed the outgoing nature of his mother and in fact Dan himself was very outgoing like her. Dan now knows that he cannot really be himself with his father. If he is, he fears that his father will reject him as he did his mother. As a result of Jack's criticism of his mother, Dan may decide to become even more like his mother. He may elect to have many girlfriends, to become a "playboy." This playboy identity was not where Dan had been headed prior to his parent's divorce. Before Jack began to constantly criticize his former wife, Dan was simply an outgoing boy. By reacting so negatively to his former wife Jack hoped Dan would also view his mother as a bad person. Just the opposite may happen, however.

On the other hand, Jack's criticism of his former wife may force Dan to be less outgoing (beginning to hate the part of himself that was like his mother). Eventually, he may even grow to distrust or dislike all women, perhaps even carrying this unstated feeling over into his own marriage. Jack would have apparently "won" the battle with his former wife. Dan would have become more like his dad. The consequences of this "victory" would be serious to the son, however. Dan would very likely suffer from low self-esteem and would be unable to sustain a meaningful relationship with the opposite sex. No parent would be gratified by this result.

How could the father have handled this situation and maintained his honesty, since he considered his former wife's life style to be immoral? Jack can be honest with Dan: "Your mother and I divorced for many reasons. I think one of the reasons might have been that what she thought was fun—drinking, dancing, going to parties—I didn't enjoy. Eventually she met some other people—some were men—who she enjoyed being with more than me. That seemed to be a big reason for our divorce. You know I don't really accept the idea of flirting with other people while being married, and this was another area where your mother and I disagreed."

In this statement Jack is truthful and stated his values and beliefs clearly. Yet he did not go on and on citing example after example of how bad Dan's mother had been, nor did Jack give Dan a long lecture on how he should live. Adolescents (children and adults, too) really tune out long lectures. Live your life by your own values; your actions will provide an excellent role model for your children. Consciously let go of trying to influence your child to accept your point of view concerning the other parent. If your former spouse is—in some ways—not a nice person, your teen will painfully experience this for himself or herself. It is sad and disappointing for children to discover that a parent cannot or will not be an adult to be admired. They do not need a possibly embittered former spouse to point this out to them.

If your teenager has strong negative feelings about the other parent (or even about you yourself), it would be helpful to have him or her speak with a professional counselor. The counselor will not try to change your child's feelings, but may be able to help your teenager accept each of you as you are— real people with strengths and weaknesses. Understanding one's parents will help the adolescent stabilize realistic expectations for the parent/child relationship.

A final word concerning a parent's influence on teenage identity formation. There are some parents who abuse or severely neglect their children. Emotional, physical, or sexual abuse leave deep scars that will permanently affect your child's adult identity. If your child has been abused or severely neglected by either yourself or your former spouse, it is crucial for you to immediately contact a professional who knows what steps to take that will help your child heal. The school guidance counselor or nurse would be a good person to contact, as would your minister, doctor, or social worker. This person may refer you to other people who have specific skills in this sensitive area. It is painful to admit that abuse has occurred in your family, but for the moment put your own pain and shame aside and act on behalf of your child.

YOUR OWN IDENTITY

As you think about your teenager's developing identity, you probably will begin to reflect upon your own identity. When adults divorce, their identity is often temporarily shattered. If for many years you have been "Greg's wife" or "Marcia's husband," it will take considerable adjustment and internal change to begin to see yourself as "Marcia, a divorced single mother" or "Greg, a divorced non-custodial father."

Changing your identity from someone's spouse to a single parent can be a complicated trial-and-error experience. Divorcing persons often "try out" new behavior in attempt to expand or change their identity. "Who am I now?" is a pressing question—almost as pressing as their adolescent's need to know about himself or herself.

New hair styles and new clothes, different friends, job change, returning to school, learning to dance, and starting a new hobby are ways divorced parents begin to define who they are now. These behaviors have an odd ring. They sound very much like expected teen behavior. Thus, you and your adolescent child may be going through a very similar process. If you find yourself immersed in thinking about what you really believe in, what you want to be, whom you admire, and how you want to look and act, then you and your child are currently on parallel paths.

As consuming as re-establishing your own identity can be, however, remember to take time to be a parent. Keep "parent" in your identity at all costs. Your child needs your interest and concern, even if he or she appears to be doing fine and to be very busy with friends and activities. This time in your life and in your child's life can be exciting and challenging, but it is also a time full of conflicting pulls and the anxiety of feeling unsure about self and future. Care for each other, listen, share, and be open to new ideas.

EXERCISE 5
Before and After

FOR YOU

Take a piece of paper and write "Who I Am" across the top. Under the heading form two columns titled, "Before the Divorce" and "Now." Next, list all the adjectives that describe you. See how many have remained the same following the divorce. Put a star by the areas of change.

After you have assessed how your identity has changed, think about whether there is anything you could do to help the transition. How might your changing identity be affecting your adolescent? Is there anything you could do to help your adolescent understand the changes?

WALT'S EXAMPLE
WHO I AM

Before the Divorce	Now
1. Welder	1. Same
2. Son	2. Same
3. Father*	3. Same, but time spent with kids is different
4. Football fan	4. Same
5. Homeowner*	5. Apartment dweller
6. Husband*	6. Ex-husband
7. Catholic	7. Same
8. German/American	8. Same

| 9. Yard worker/gardener* | 9. No place to garden |
| 10. Man sexually attracted to women | 10. Same |

My Reaction to the Changes in My Identity:

I am surprised by the many things that are the same for me. Really, only my living arrangements and marital status have changed. I guess I really am missing my yard and garden. Perhaps in the spring I will look into renting a garden plot or do some outdoor hiking. I will talk with the kids about my desire to continue to be involved in their lives—maybe I'll invite them to join me in my outdoor activities. I must be careful not to expect them to like the outdoors as much as I do. I also realize that it is important to me to recognize that I am still sexually attracted to women. I need to let the kids (especially the boys?) see that part of me.

Comment

Doing this exercise helped Walt feel better about his life. He realized that there were many aspects of his identity that had not been affected by the divorce. He committed himself to the parenting role, realizing that he was still a father, although the time spent with his three adolescent children would be different. Walt was surprised at how much he missed the yard and garden and this discovery helped him begin to plan ways of replacing his interest in the outdoors and sharing them with his teenagers.

Walt also had an insight into his own sexuality and its possible effects on his adolescents. He understood that it was important for him to recognize that he was still sexually attracted to women and to share that identity with his children. He wondered whether that was especially true for his two sons.

EXERCISE FOR AGES 12-14

Prepare a short questionnaire titled "Who I Am." Have about four open-ended questions such as:

1. If I could do anything when I grow up it would be _____.
2. My family is _____.
3. My appearance is _____.
4. The quality I like best about myself is _____.

Mail this questionnaire to your adolescent with a letter explaining that you are very interested in communicating about important topics and that you are experimenting with new ways of knowing each other.

Dear Julie,

Surprise! The enclosed questionnaire is from me, your mom. I know how very important it is for us to keep communications open, and I thought this new "questionnaire" method might be fun. Please take a minute and complete the enclosed questions. You can put the answers on my dresser when you are finished.

We can also talk about your ideas, Julie, and not just use the questionnaire. I don't want to pry, but I hope you will be able to share some of "who you are" with me. I will share my ideas about myself with you too, if you want to know.

What a mixed-up year this has been with the divorce and Dad moving so far away! Now your mother is turning weird and sending you questionnaires! Who ever said our family was dull?

I love you, Julie.
Mom

P.S. If you want, send me a questionnaire.

EXERCISE FOR AGES 15-18

Make an appointment with your son's or daughter's high school counselor to review any results of aptitude/interest tests and to explore possible future plans: i.e., courses to take, post-high-school direction, etc. Ask your child to attend the session with you (but go alone if he or she is hesitant or embarrassed).

The purpose of this meeting is not to pressure your child or the school to perform better. It is to help your child begin to think about options for his or her life. It is also to enlist the guidance counselor as a resource to help your child in this important area.

At this meeting you might tell the counselor that there has been a divorce and how the divorce might impact your child. For example, if financial resources are very limited, the counselor needs to know this in helping your child think about college choices. Please communicate clearly with your child that you are doing this to help him or her with planning for the future, but that ultimately these decisions will have to be his or hers.

Such a meeting is a very important parental responsibility—worth taking a half day off work. If you and your former spouse have a good co-parenting relationship, your might invite him or her to join you.

TABLE TOPICS

1. What do you think is special about our family?
2. In what ways do you see yourself as a "religious" person?
3. If you could live anywhere, where would it be, and why? Five years from now, what do you think you will be doing? What would you like to be doing?

CHAPTER 6

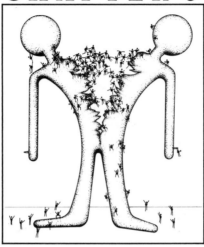

YOUR ADOLESCENT'S EMERGING SEXUALITY

"My mom doesn't want my boyfriend Scott to come over to my dad's house. We fight about this all the time."

> Debbie, a sixteen-year-old

"Why do you think she has this rule?"

> Debbie's counselor

"Oh, I'm sure she thinks he'll get ideas from Dad and his girlfriend!"

> Debbie

As their children move into puberty, parents cannot help but be aware of changes in their teenagers' bodies, interests, and attitudes. Many of these normal developmental changes are related to becoming a sexual adult. For some parents, it is very difficult to accept their child's emerging sexuality. This difficulty is sometimes compounded by a divorce, with its added issues of custody, visitation, and parental dating or remarriage.

The inability to openly deal with sexual values and concerns creates distance and distrust between adolescent and parent, problems that a divorce can acerbate. Obviously, parent-child misunderstandings and tensions related to sexual concerns occur in "intact" families as well as in divorced families—it is one of the hallmarks of the teenage years. For a parent trying to adjust to a divorce, however, the additional stress of coping with an adolescent's new sexuality may feel overwhelming.

AN UNCOMFORTABLE TOPIC

Historically and culturally, we as a nation have been very closed and private about sexuality. For the greater part of our history, moral and religious leaders have stressed sexual abstinence before marriage as the only morally acceptable decision. These authorities have proclaimed sex-related rules ranging from the type of clothes that are appropriate to the proper sexual positions during intercourse.

During the past few decades, these beliefs about sexuality have begun to be questioned, even by those same moral and religious leaders. More and more people see sex as a natural component of being fully human, as an important way for two people to express their love for each other—sometimes even before or outside the institution of marriage. Even those who maintain the exclusivity of sex in marriage have rejected the idea that sex and sexuality is somehow intrinsically evil or even something embarrassing to discuss.

Beginning in the 1960's, we have witnessed a "sexual revolution" in which a substantial number of people openly and publicly denounced any sexual restrictions or control. There has been a barrage of radio and T.V. shows, books, movies, and newspaper and magazine articles openly exploring a variety of sexual attitudes and practices. Many formerly held beliefs have been challenged and, in some cases, have collapsed.

Most of you with teenagers today were raised by parents who themselves subscribed to the morality of sexual repression and control. In your own adolescent years, these instincts were often internalized in your own moral structure. You yourselves, however, were probably young adults in the midst of the "sexual revolution." You may even have participated in the "liberation" of feelings and practices that it implied. For many of you, therefore, sex is an especially confusing, ambiguous subject—especially when it involves your own children.

PARENTS AND TEENS

Today's parents of teenagers find themselves in a vulnerable, uncharted position. Most of these parents never discussed sexual concerns with their own parents. Therefore they have had no role model for open sexual discussion. Some still feel awkward about their own sexuality and do not feel safe discussing it—especially with their own children.

Other parents hold very conflicting views on sexuality (believing, for example, that it is all right for grownups like themselves to engage in sex outside of marriage but not for their children to do so; or practicing birth control themselves while preaching against it to their teens.) Some parents even believe that sex-related topics are handled sufficiently in school or that a child's sexuality is a private concern, inappropriate as a topic of conversation. Others leave the entire matter to the other parent—sometimes a particularly dangerous tack in a divorce situation where the entire subject can be avoided by both parents. Due to their own conflicting, ambivalent beliefs and lack of role models, it is often extremely difficult for these parents to discuss these issues with their adolescent children—just when those children are desperate for information, example, and direction on the matter.

The fact is, no matter what your own hangups or difficulties about discussing sex, it is a critically important area for your teenager. No matter how awkward you may feel, your child needs your input in developing his or her emerging sexuality.

Debbie's mother, Kay, never articulated her feelings about her former husband's infidelity during their marriage and his string of woman friends after their divorce. Instead of trying to discuss these feelings with her daughter, Kay instead tried to insist on the unenforceable rule that Debbie's boyfriend could not visit her when she was with her father. Rather than using the differences in values between her and her former husband as a starting place for discussion with Debbie, Kay created what her daughter viewed as an unreasonable rule that provided another occasion for a fight.

Debbie, on the other hand, was certain that her mother's position had to do with Debbie's emerging sexuality. Debbie could see clearly the difference between her mother's and her father's sexual values and practices. She needed to explore those values with her mother so that she could come to her own conclusions about how she would live her own life.

Kay was afraid that her former husband's example would lead Debbie to conclude that there was nothing wrong with extramarital sex. She also worried that if Debbie did begin a sexual relationship with her boyfriend Scott, she might get pregnant and ruin her plans to go to college. Yet Kay worried that if she discussed birth control with her daughter, it would be seen as condoning pre-marital sex. Instead of dealing with all of these feelings and fears with her daughter, however, Kay spent her energy trying to prevent Debbie's boyfriend from visiting her at her father's house. Not only was this strategy doomed to fail, but it prevented the mother from using the opportunity to engage in a truly meaningful dialogue with her daughter.

DISCUSSING SEX

If your teenager has never raised the issue of sexuality, don't believe it is because of disinterest. Assume instead that he or she is getting information elsewhere. Adolescents are often no more comfortable discussing sexuality than their parents. Some teens sense that the topic is taboo at home, and so they discuss their concerns with others—usually their friends. They also get information from reading magazines or from television. Only occasionally are they presented with decent sex education in school, and even this is mostly of a technical nature and does not necessarily reflect the values that a parent might like to engender.

Sources of information on sex available to teenagers may not be very reliable or may only present one perspective. The only way to ensure that your child is getting a good, value-based education about sexuality is to do it yourself. There is no substitute for frank and open discussion between parent and teenage child regarding sexuality.

There are important limits and reservations to such discussions, however. First, it is important for each party—both parent and child—to retain some privacy about his or her own intimate sexual life. Adolescent children do *not* want or need to know about their parents' sex lives—either before, during, or after their marriage. They want and need to know facts about normal adult sexuality, including health considerations. They want and need to discuss values related to responsible sexual behavior and to explore how sex relates to love and marriage. Your child wants to know what your values are and why you hold them.

In turn, your adolescent wants and needs to share his or her sexual concerns and values with you. Remember, however, that adolescence is a time of exploring and choosing the values by which one will live as an adult. Your child's ideas about sexuality may not always agree with yours. You must be able to listen without lecturing or overreacting. Your child will not tell you of every kiss, hug, or fondle. Engaging in such private, personal intimacies with others outside the family is one way a youngster begins to separate from the family of origin. To share such activity with parents could seriously impede the process of maturation. Likewise, for a parent to share too much of his or her own sexual experience might inhibit a child's normal sexual development.

What is needed in a healthy parent-child relationship is the ability to talk about sexual topics while allowing each person the proper degree of personal privacy.

VALUES AND SEXUALITY

Values shape the beliefs upon which we base our actions. If a person openly speaks the truth (as it is known), he or she values honesty. If a person spends money on jewelry, he or she values appearance and beauty.

Much of human behavior has a sexual component: flirting, driving powerful cars, talking loud, kissing, masturbating, etc. All of us have beliefs and values related to these topics. It is the act of sexual intercourse, however, that stirs up the most intense feelings. Here are some categories related to sexual intercourse, matching the values people hold and the sexual actions or behavior that might result:

1. Commitment.

The value of commitment in relationships leads many people to believe in marital exclusivity or monogamous marriage. Sexual intercourse, therefore, should take place only in marriage. This also leads some people to believe that marriage is a lifetime commitment and to oppose divorce.

2. Love.

The value of love in relationships results in the belief that sexual intercourse should be the culmination of a loving relationship. For people who hold this value, the idea of "casual" or "recreational" sex is immoral. Yet such people can envision sex outside of marriage in certain circumstances.

3. Pleasure.

Some people view sexual intercourse as pure pleasure, involving no marriage/love/commitment whatsoever. Sex is a natural, biological act, and it is unnecessary to consider emotions such as love or commitment. These people see sex between consenting adults as perfectly acceptable at any time.

In addition to these three basic values regarding intercourse, some people add a fourth category based on age and maturity and the willingness to accept responsibility for one's actions. Some people regard engaging in sexual intercourse under any one of the three categories listed above as acceptable for older adults (the age differs greatly from person to person), but not for younger people—especially teenagers.

THE WHYS OF BELIEF

Before parents can speak with their teenage children about sex, they themselves must understand which of these values they hold and why. If their own sexual behavior reflects their values or beliefs, they will probably feel comfortable talking about them. If their own behavior is inconsistent with their beliefs, however, they may feel somewhat guilty sharing their views with their children.

Adolescence is a time of development in which the child is testing and clarifying personal values. Children at this age look to their parents to share their beliefs—not only about *how* one should act but also *why.* Explaining the why of beliefs is an important dimension of establishing an honest relationship and need not be viewed by a parent as "defending" oneself. If a parent is unable to explain "why" a certain set of values is held, a teenager may well look elsewhere for his or her answers.

As Kay began to examine her beliefs toward sexual intercourse, she realized that she strongly believed that it should be reserved for marriage. It was obvious that her former husband did not.

Kay had attended Catholic parochial grade and high schools, where she had been taught that intercourse was only part of a loving, lifelong commitment. When she was a young adult, she had observed the sexual practices of her friends and others, who no longer considered sexual intercourse extremely special. Kay wanted sex to remain special in her life, and her observations of others had helped to re-confirm her childhood lesson: it was only with the commitment of marriage that Kay could share herself with another.

Yet Kay was now a divorced, single parent—something that she had never anticipated. After her divorce had been final for several years, she began to date again, but she decided she would not have sexual intercourse with any man she dated unless and until they were to get married. So even though she was divorced, Kay kept her beliefs in her basic values regarding sex and lived those values in her actions.

With the help of a counselor, Kay began to share these values with her daughter Debbie. They had their first open discussion about sex one evening when neither of them had to rush off. Kay experienced some difficulty getting started, but the more they talked the easier it became. At first, Debbie also seemed reluctant to talk about this topic, because she feared her mother was just going to give her a lecture. Instead, Kay shared her own feelings about her value choices—including how difficult it sometimes was to live them.

Kay told Debbie that she wished her daughter would agree with her values about love and sex but that she realized that Debbie would have to come to her own decisions about her life, just as Kay had. Kay admitted that the reason she didn't want Debbie's boyfriend Scott to visit at her father's house was that she disapproved of her former husband's life style and was afraid that it would influence the two teenagers.

"Oh, Mom," Debbie said, "Scott's parents are stricter than you are and Scott thinks Dad is terribly mixed up." Kay was both surprised and relieved—and a little proud—to hear her daughter's maturity and common sense. This conversation opened the door for other discussions. The bond of trust began to grow between mother and daughter. Rather than laying down what appear to be arbitrary rules, Kay is beginning to talk about her own values and to listen to her daughter's emerging beliefs.

This has not eliminated all Kay's fears for her daughter, but she has realized that ultimately Debbie has control over her own sexual practices and that Kay can best help Debbie's sexual development by being clear about her own values and being willing to share them.

DIVORCE AND ADOLESCENT SEXUALITY

When parents divorce, each of their post-divorce life styles may reflect different values or beliefs about sexuality. One parent may feel it is all right to engage in sexual relations with a person if both parties are attracted to each other. For this person, sex does not have anything to do with marriage and commitment. The other parent may believe that sex should be reserved for marriage. Thus the stage is set for an intense "value war," a war where the ultimate victims may be the children.

Imagine some of the scenes and conversations a teenager might experience: "You can't go to your father's apartment. He has no morals and will sleep with any whore off the street." Or: "Your mother is living in a different century! She doesn't know how to be open and sharing with her feelings." Off to court: "Judge, I do not want my children to go on vacation with their father and his girlfriend. I don't want them exposed to such immoral behavior." Answer: "Judge, my friend will have a separate room on vacation. I want my children to share a good time—their mother never takes them anywhere."

Even if they are not physically present, children are very aware of conflict between their parents. Teenagers especially are quick to realize when this conflict is about sexual values. For an adolescent trying to define his or her own sexuality, experiencing such hostile parental differences on this issue may impede the natural development process. The child may overidentify with one parent against the other or may feel split between the two. Either position places the adolescent in a precarious emotional position.

Unless a child's well-being is seriously at risk (such as suspected abuse, exposure to drugs, or other risks to safety), having parents fighting or going to court over personal values or beliefs is usually more emotionally damaging to the children than the issue itself. Former spouses must be willing and able to let go of the need to control each other's behavior, if not for their own sake then for that of their children. This does not mean that you must like or approve of your former spouse's values or behavior. You must develop some confidence, however, in your teenager's own ability to observe and weigh the differences in parental beliefs and actions, arriving at his or her independent value structure.

Some divorced parents are not in conflict over post-divorce sexual practices, for they hold similar values and support each other. This is certainly helpful for the children. If there are differences, however, it is the teenager-becoming-an-adult who is going to have to sort it out and decide for himself or herself.

Another area of difficulty for adolescents of divorced parents is to tolerate a parent having a new sexual relationship—even if it is accompanied by remarriage. At a time when the teenager is experiencing his or her personal sexual awakening, being exposed to intense sexuality on the part of one or both parents may prove overstimulating. There will also be confusion by teenagers regarding the questions of love and commitment. "If you said you'd love Mom until death do you part," they might say, "how can you now say you'll love Joan forever?"

The teenager may react to renewed parental sexuality by becoming sexually active too soon or, oppositely, repressing all sexual feelings.

It is healthy for children to know their parents are loving, sexual people. This provides a positive adult role model. Parents, however, should practice discretion and take their children's emotions into account. Don't, for example, disappear into your bedroom for two hours in the middle of the afternoon while your son or daughter is watching television in the next room. Monitor your behavior and use common sense.

EXERCISE 6
Speaking about (SHH!) Sex

FOR YOU

Choose an aspect of sexuality—other than sexual intercourse—and identify your values or beliefs related to that practice. Birth control, homosexuality, pornography, and masturbation are examples you might explore. List what you believe about that issue, and then why you believe as you do (where your beliefs came from). Then list what (tentative) values or beliefs you think your teenagers holds toward this sex-related practice, and then why you think your child believes as he or she does. (Remember, you are only *speculating* about your child's beliefs—we can never read another person's mind.)

Finally, see how closely you perceive you and your teenager are in agreement and how you feel about your differences.

ANN'S EXAMPLE

Area of Sexuality: Birth control

My Value/Belief: Abstinence until ready to assume the responsibility for a child.

Why I Believe This: I think abortion is immoral and causes trauma to the woman. Therefore if an unmarried young woman gets pregnant I believe the couple should marry and raise the child or else they should give the baby up for adoption. I am a practicing Catholic and follow the teachings of the Church regarding birth control. Since the "natural family planning" method of birth control is not foolproof, I feel abstinence is the best method of birth control.

What I Think Kevin Believes: Use of condoms as the best method of birth control, even though he knows they are not completely effective.

Why Kevin Believes This: Kevin has many friends who hold values that are different from mine. I'm not sure if any of the boys are sexually active yet, but I think if they had the opportunity to have a sexual relationship—even at the age of sixteen—they would. I think Kevin would too. None of the boys wants to get married, however, and with condoms so advertised and available, I think they would use them.

How I Feel: I wonder sometimes if I am too "old-fashioned." Kevin sometimes says I don't understand how things really are today. Yet I know how I feel and I like my own values. I hope I am having an influence on Kevin. I guess if he is going to be sexually active I would prefer he use condoms rather than nothing (especially given the possibility of AIDS), but I still believe abstinence would be best for him. Maybe I can figure out an opportunity to talk with him about why I feel that way. I love Kevin and am very proud of him. He really is a great kid. I've got to remember to tell him that, too.

Comment

Ann is a forty-two-year-old divorced mother with custody of her sixteen-year-old son, Kevin. For Ann, the most helpful aspect of doing this exercise was identifying her ambivalence toward the whole area of birth control. On the one hand, she realized that she was very clear and committed to her own values on the issues of pre-marital sex, abortion, and birth control. Yet she also was aware that her son may well not share her values and that if he were to be sexually active she might well want him to use some form of birth control. (Ann admitted to herself that the AIDS crisis had introduced an entirely new factor into the birth control consideration.)

Ann also recognized that her rather strict views also differed from those of many of her own friends, and she felt a certain sense of relief in accepting and reaffirming her own values. This also gave her the freedom to understand that others (even her own son) might not share all her beliefs—and that this too was "okay." She did determine, however, to share her values again with Kevin—although she reminded herself to also tell her son how much she loved and admired him.

The one thing that Ann avoided in this exercise was any reflection on the values that her former husband, Frank—Kevin's father—might hold. This may have been because their divorce was very recent and she felt that she did not have the emotional distance yet to consider Frank's impact on their son, or she might have felt that Frank was going to leave the entire question of sex for her to explain to Kevin. In either case, it probably would be helpful to Ann to spend some time thinking about her former spouse's influence on this important aspect of Kevin's sexual development.

EXERCISE FOR AGES 12-14

Conversation time: When you are driving alone with your teen, ask him or her to tell you what guidelines single parents (specifically you) should follow when dating. (Have the conversation in the car because your teenager is captured in one place: there is no escape to the telephone or T.V. If necessary, pull the plug on the car radio!) Keep a relaxed attitude. If he or she has no ideas, let the subject drop. At least you have begun to establish an atmosphere of openness. Perhaps later the child will bring the question up again.

You might start the conversation by saying "Parents always have ideas about what their children should and shouldn't do. I thought it would be interesting to find out what you think about me dating someone."

Remember: you are in charge of deciding about what you will and will not do regarding dates (or sex, for that matter). Getting input from your teenager will allow you to take his or her feelings into consideration.

EXERCISE FOR AGES 15-18

Movie time: Buy some popcorn and rent the videotape of *Shoot the Moon* or *Twice in a Lifetime*. (If you don't have a VCR, ask a friend or relative if you can borrow theirs for a weekend or watch for either movie on television.) Both of these excellent films deal with divorce, its impact on family members, and parental sexuality. Watch the film with your teenager and then discuss how you each felt about the movie parents' romantic involvements.

TABLE TOPICS

1. How prevalent is pregnancy at the local high school? What happens to the girls who become pregnant? What about their boyfriends?
2. Do you feel differently about my dating than about your dad (mom) doing the same? Why?
3. Do you think I will/should ever remarry?

CHAPTER 7

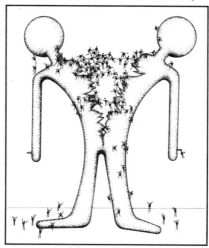

VISITATION, CUSTODY, CHILD SUPPORT, ETC.

"This is your weekend to visit Dad."

Michael's mother, Sue

"No way. It's so boring at his apartment. I'm not going."

Michael, a sixteen-year-old

For many parents, the process of divorce is never complete. It continues for a lifetime over issues relating to the children—the only cord still linking the couple. After a divorce is finalized, former spouses supposedly have nothing left to fight about. They, their lawyers, and finally a judge have created in the final decree the rules and guidelines for the division of properties and for the care of the children. The divorce-decree guidelines are to be adhered to by both parties and were designed so that each parent's rights to spend time with the child have been protected.

Many people, however, cannot "let go" of the conflict they have been engaged in during their marriage and the divorce process. They continue to fight, primarily over issues related to the children. Some decide they do not agree with the divorce decree and openly defy it. Some hold that the final decree was vague and continue to fight over interpretation. In many cases, new circumstances arise that were not covered in the decree, which leads to new fights. None of this is helpful to their children. Parents fight, fight, fight ... and the children listen, observe, and become increasingly anxious.

For divorced parents of teenagers, this tension is increased by the addition of a new element to an already volatile mix: adolescents can—and probably will—have independent, strongly held ideas about issues that affect them—such as visitation schedules, custody, and money concerns. The views of teenagers may add complexity to an already unsettling situation.

VISITATION

Michael's father, Bruce, did not know what to do or think when his former wife informed him that his son was resisting visiting him as had been agreed in the divorce decree. Was his son refusing to visit because Bruce's former wife Sue really didn't want Michael to come? Did Michael really dislike his father? Or was this normal teenage behavior?

Bruce was angry, hurt, and confused. Should he go to court to try to force Michael to comply with the visitation schedule? Should he back off and let his son alone while he went through a "stage"?

Bruce and Sue had divorced four years before when Michael was twelve. Sue had been awarded custody of the children—Michael and his seven-year-old sister Natalie. The visitation schedule agreed upon stated that Bruce would have the children every other weekend, three weeks in the summer, and alternating holidays.

For the first two years, the plan appeared to work very well. Bruce would pick up the children Friday night, spend the weekend at his two bedroom apartment on the other side of town, and return them before dinner on Sunday. He often planned things to do such as going to the movies, cross-country skiing, and bike riding. Occasionally, one of the children would be ill and stay home with their mother, but even then the other child had seemed to come willingly.

In the middle of his first year in high school, however, Michael began calling Bruce on the Wednesday or Thursday before the visit, stating that he wanted to go to the high school game or a friend's party or some such activity. Bruce would sometimes respond by telling Michael to come anyway—that he could always attend other games or parties but he only had one father. (The "guilt trip" approach.) Other times, Bruce would make complex arrangements such as picking Michael up on Friday, driving him back for an event, and then picking him up afterward and returning to the apartment. This meant that Bruce and Natalie would spend most of Saturday evening driving or going to a movie near the high school so they could accommodate Michael's schedule. (The "martyr act" or "complicated arrangement" approach.)

How Bruce responded depended on how he was feeling at the time. He kept hoping that Michael would respond positively to one of his approaches and that visits would return to normal. Instead, Michael began to withdraw even further from his father. When they were together, Michael didn't seem as spontaneous and open as in the past, and Bruce felt that he knew his son less and less.

At about this same time, Sue had filed a petition in court for an increase in child support because Bruce had been promoted at his company and had received a considerable salary increase. Bruce was angry with his former wife for going back to court without first trying to negotiate directly with him. He also felt that possibly Michael's refusal to visit him was related to the parental child-support battle.

The truth is that most of Michael's reluctance to be with his father had *little or nothing to do* with the relations between his parents. In the years since his parents had divorced, Michael had become a teenager who was expressing a very natural desire to do teenage activities with his teenage friends. Adolescents must begin the process of separating from their parents, and to help them separate there is an unspoken adolescent rule: "Don't be seen doing things with your parents. It's not *cool!*"

Bruce's fluctuating responses, which were based on his own feelings and needs, did not help Michael separate gracefully. Michael began to dread speaking with his father, then he started to become angry with him, and finally he played his trump card—he refused to visit him. The child support issue was at most a minor factor influencing Michael's actions. He did know that his parents were in court fighting over money, and this may have reinforced his growing resentment of Bruce. Primarily, however, Michael just wanted to do what all teenagers want to do: hang out (without his parents).

With help from a counselor, Bruce eventually was able to get Michael to sit down and discuss his feelings about visitation. The boy was leery at first, but he finally began to realize that his father had a real desire to understand his son's needs. When he heard his dad's genuine interest and concern for him, Michael became a willing participant in searching for a solution to the impasse.

Michael and Bruce worked out the following arrangement. Bruce would call Michael on Wednesday or Thursday of each week. During these phone calls, father and son would talk about what was going on in their lives. Bruce would ask Michael if he had some time or wanted to get together during the upcoming weekend. If Michael said okay, they would make plans, but if Michael was too busy—or even if he just wanted to stay home—Bruce would honor his decision. Finally, they agreed that if Bruce had a special event he wanted Michael to share with him, such as attending his grandmother's birthday party, he would tell Michael as far in advance as possible and specifically state, "Michael, it is very important to me that you go with me." Then Michael would make every effort to honor his father's wishes. The two are currently making this plan work, and both feel better about their relationship.

This story has a constructive, happy ending. A much different outcome might have been written, however, if Bruce had been unwilling to look at this problem from Michael's adolescent perspective. The major factor in resolving divorce visitation or custody concerns related to teenagers lies here.

CUSTODY

Courts are usually mandated by law to award custody on the basis of what it judges to be the best interest of the child. There is a current, growing trend to award joint custody, so both parents have the right to provide input into their child's life. In most cases, however, one parent is given primary physical custody of the child and a joint parenting agreement is constructed that spells out visitation rights for the other parent. Custody problems arise, however, when parents have different opinions regarding their children's best interests and cannot agree on a co-parenting arrangement.

Who knows what is in the best interest of a child? Who decides custody? The parents—each with different ideas, which may be based on their own needs and desires rather than the child's? The child—torn between love for both parents and emotionally and intellectually incapable of knowing what is best? A mental health professional—who may be getting only part or one side of the story? The judge—limited by the constraints of the legal system and often carrying a large load of similar cases? If there is disagreement about custody, input may be gathered from all of these sources.

The best solution for the child is obviously for the two parents to put aside their animosity and selfish interests and to work out a solution that is truly healthy for each individual child. Ultimately, however, the final divorce decree must be decided or approved by a judge. Although this may seem to be handing over an important decision to an "outsider," it must be done to ensure objectivity and protect the interests of the children.

Some parents and children believe that judges will let the child, once he or she reaches the age of fourteen, decide the custody arrangement. This so-called "rule of fourteen" is a legal myth. It is true that most divorce law states that children's wishes are to be considered in custody decisions. As children become older, most judges give more weight to the expressed wishes of a child—and for good reason. A child's cognitive ability and reasoning power are more developed at fourteen than at six. Judges also recognize that it is difficult, if not impossible, to force adolescents to accept living arrangements against their will. If there is not a "good enough" relationship between a parent and child by the teen years, it is impossible to create one by court order. Judges also recognize the need for adolescents to spend considerable time with their friends and peers.

There are other questionable reasons why a teenager may express a specific custody preference. One parent may have a disproportionate positive or negative income, and the child may be lured by the desire for the wealthier life style. One parent may be more permissive, with few or no rules, and the adolescent may want to live in an environment where that parent is in control. In these cases, the court must explore the existing relationships with each parent more intensively. One parent must not be allowed to "buy" his or her children with money or favors.

Many teenage children do express a desire to live with one parent or the other, and that parent's financial position is not a factor. Others reasons include feeling more comfortable with that parent, knowing that parent has more time available, or wanting to remain in the family home near friends and school. In these cases, the adolescent can present to parents or the court a balanced and thoughtful discussion of custody considerations.

These are some questions that divorcing parents with the best interest of their children at heart should consider before deciding on custodial arrangements:

- With which parent does the child feel free to express ideas?
- Which parent has the best understanding of an adolescent?
- Through the years, which parent has provided primary emotional support for the child?
- Which parent can provide a safe, consistent home life?

If the answer to most of these questions is both parents, then your child is very lucky. You probably are a divorcing family that would be ideal for joint custody. If the answer is predominantly one parent, then that parent will usually be the one the teenager will voice a preference to be with and, in fact, that parent will usually provide the best family care for the child.

This may be very difficult for the non-custodial parent—who also loves the child and wants to continue to live with him or her—to accept. If the other parent has established a stronger bond with a child, however, it is better not to fight for custody but to spend one's energy and money in more positive ways of supporting the child. Be available to your teenager when he or she needs you. Take an interest in his or her activities. Be willing to be flexible—for adolescents' schedules are often busy. Plan some fun vacations. Provide extra money if you have it. Do these things because you care for your child, *not* to win him or her away from the other parent! The result will be a positive relationship with your child that will continue into his or her adult life.

CHANGES IN CUSTODY

As children enter adolescence or grow older, they sometimes want to change custody arrangements. Seth's parents divorced when he was nine. Seth's mother, Mary, was awarded custody of the three children. For several years, visitations with their father, Stan, went very smoothly. When Seth was fourteen, however Stan remarried and moved across the country to New Jersey. Seth soon began speaking to his mother about wanting to live with his father.

Mary did not automatically jump to the conclusion that Stan was "putting him up to this," and she did not take Seth's request to mean he didn't love her. Mother and son explored Seth's reasons for wanting to live with Stan. Seth said he had lived with Mary for five years and now he thought it would be fair to spend some time—the next four years before he went out on his own—with his father. Seth also missed his father.

Through the years they had been very close and had done a lot of activities together. Father and son had very similar personalities and even looked a lot alike.

After thinking about Seth's request for three months—thus giving him plenty of time to change his mind—Mary and Stan agreed to the change of custody. Seth now lives in New Jersey with his father and stepmother and comes to his mother's home every summer and several holidays per year. Seth's younger brother and sister continue to live with their mother and visit their father.

This custody change took place without acrimony. Seth feels understood and supported by both parents. Such a desire to change custody is not an uncommon occurrence. It is part of the healthy process of adolescent identity formation and separation from parents. Do not overreact if it happens or take it as a personal rebuff. Take such a request seriously. Try to explore and understand why the request is being made. If changing custody appears to be in the best interest of the child, act on it. Such a move may be painful, but it will build a bond of understanding and acceptance with your teenager that will last a lifetime.

Not all change of custody requests should be honored, however. Many such demands are made by adolescents when they are upset or angry, and these should be allowed to cool before they are addressed. There are also many instances in which an adolescent may be motivated to request a custody arrangement for reasons that are really not in his or her best interest. For example, seventeen-year-old Kathy returned to her custodial mother's home after a four-week out-of-state visit with her non-custodial father, Max. She announced to her mother, Jeanine, that she wanted to move to her father's home to finish her junior and senior high school years. Although Kathy claimed that she just wanted to spend more time with her father, the truth was that she had met a cute boy at her father's. In addition, Max—who was still angry with Jeanine—had promised Kathy a new car if she moved to his home.

Jeanine refused to let Kathy move, and Max took the matter back to divorce court. Beyond Kathy's wishes, the judge had several other important factors to consider. Kathy was doing very well at her current high school, she had a number of good friends, and was involved in school activities. Kathy also had a younger sister, eight-year-old Alice, who was not requesting a custody change. Finally, Kathy and her mother had always had a good relationship prior to the recent visit with her father. In this case, the judge denied the custody change.

After the decision, Jeanine told Kathy that when she finished high school, she could choose a college near her father's home—perhaps living with Max and attending the local community college. After a day or two of anger, Kathy accepted both the decision and her mother's attempts at compromise. She had a happy junior and senior year, continued to visit her father, and did eventually move to be near him during college. Even at seventeen, however, her wishes were not considered a significant enough reason to change the existing custody arrangement.

PARENTS WHO ARE UNAVAILABLE

There are situations in which the non-custodial parent establishes a very separate life after a divorce and has little or no contact with his or her children. Adolescents who discuss this type of post-divorce parental relationship often appear callous and unconcerned: "I really don't care if he comes to my graduation. In fact, I really don't want him there. Who cares? He's out of my life." The night of the graduation, this same child searches the audience to see if she spots her father: "Does he really care for me? Does he love me enough to show up, even though he will have to face Mom and her new husband?"

If Dad does not show up, the sick feeling of being deserted by one's own parent grows. The adolescent continues to exhibit a "who cares, anyway" attitude, because it is too painful to experience full force the sadness that parental non-interest triggers.

All children—*teenagers included*—want and need their parents' concern and love. They want their parents to be interested in them, even if they do not have the time or inclination to be equally interested in the parent. Adolescence is a very tumultuous time and it is normal for a child to think primarily of himself or herself, secondarily of peers, and—a distant third—of parents and family.

101

The custodial parent who senses that a teenager is feeling deserted by the other parent has several options. The first is to look at your own behavior. Rethink the divorce process and see if there were emotional barriers created that may have resulted in your former spouse pulling back from the children. If you are indeed part of the cause of the absence of the other parent, you might need to alter your behavior for the sake of your children. Some non-custodial parents find it painful to see their children because of the tension involved in making the arrangements or the hostility they encounter from their former spouse during the pickup or return. Some deal with this tension by complete withdrawal.

Sometimes the problem lies in your teenager's own attitudes and communication pattern. Is he or she telling the non-custodial parent that it is no big deal—that "I really don't care"? If the other parent believes this is true, then the scene is set for a disintegrating relationship.

You may be able to help your child express his or her feelings in a more honest way. You might say, "I know you are saying you don't care if you see your mom, but I really think you miss her. Your mother doesn't know how to express her feelings very well, so perhaps you need to try to open up communication with her by calling (or writing a note) and telling her that you wish you two could get together once in a while." Besides giving some practical advice, this approach will grant your child your permission to reach out to the other parent.

After exploring your own attitudes and encouraging your child to communicate directly with the other parent, there is little else you should do to help their relationship. It is very important that you *not* get into the role of the mediator between your former spouse and your children. This may be a tempting role because it offers a lot of power and continues your relationship with your former spouse—no matter how poor it might be.

If your former spouse has little or no interest in his or her children, then he or she may be the type of person who cannot really care for others—even his or her own children. This is very sad for your children, for you yourself, and maybe even for your former spouse. If you believe this to be true, your child might benefit from speaking with a professional counselor about this issue. The therapist will want to explore the situation in depth, perhaps even meeting with the non-custodial parent if this is possible. If the counselor cannot promote a relationship between the child and the absent parent, he or she will try to help the child understand why certain people are unable to be parents and the wide range of emotions this realization promotes. Such work should be done by a trained psychotherapist or other mental health professional. If you attempt it on your own, there is a good chance the child will end up blaming you for the failure of your former spouse.

A final word of caution: There are parents who are psychologically unstable and who emotionally, physically, or sexually abuse their children. If your child has experienced an abusive parental relationship, there will be deep psychological wounds. Both you and your child will need to have professional help in healing. The counselor will also help to work out a visitation plan with the abusive parent that is both helpful and safe. Even in this case, it is important that the child maintain some sort of relationship with that parent. There are instances, however, when the child feels he or she cannot see an abusive parent until he or she is older, stronger, or safer—if ever. If an adolescent expresses such concern, one must listen very carefully to him or her—even if it means going back into court. In most such instances, the court will honor the child's wishes. As the child enters adulthood, he or she is then free to rebuild the parent-child relationship, if it is desired.

CHILD SUPPORT

The divorce decree establishes an amount of money the non-custodial parent (usually the father) is required to pay the custodial parent to help support the child. This is generally an amount agreed upon by the parties. When the parties are unable to agree the amount is fixed by the court. After the divorce, the easiest way to avoid conflict in this area is for the non-custodial parent to pay the required amount in a timely fashion. A good record of child support payments tends to reduce conflict.

If you are the non-custodial parent, it is critical to keep in mind that the money is helping provide a secure home for your children. You also must accept the fact that you cannot dictate how the money is to be spent. The money is given to the custodial parent to use as needed. If you remarry or incur other financial responsibilities after the divorce, *this does not reduce your responsibility to your children.* If your income drops, substantially affecting your ability to pay, speak to an attorney to help modify the amount. Do not stop or reduce payment without seeking legal advice.

When the child-support check comes late or not at all it can create an upsetting situation not only for the custodial parent but for the children as well—and teenagers are often much more attuned to this issue than their younger siblings. This money if often necessary to pay for essential living expenses, such as rent, food, utilities, and clothing, as well as "non-essential" expenditures like prom clothes or automobile insurance. When a non-custodial parent fails to meet these obligations, bill collectors may begin to call and utility services shut off. This type of financial crisis creates tension, worry, and embarrassment for children. In addition to feeling worried, they may feel angry at both parents for failing to care for them.

103

Money is often used by people to control others. Withholding child support or demanding more child support may be a way of trying to get at your former spouse. If you are having conflicts over child support, try to determine what really is behind the conflict. Are you trying to manipulate your former spouse? Do you resent paying money and having no say over the spending? It is normal if you are paying child support to be incensed if there is little or no recognition from your former spouse or your children about the child-support money. Paying child support, however, is another cost of divorce. To be at peace with yourself, you need to become gradually reconciled with this obligation—whether the support is recognized or not.

There are cases in which the custodial parent will request an increase in child support or the non-payment of child support continues to be an issue. In these situations, both parents must avoid involving the children in their continuing legal controversy. Children—again especially teenagers—usually know something is going on, however, and should be told the truth if they ask about the problem. In no case should the children be made to feel that they have caused the problem. A parent might tell a child: "Mom (or Dad) and I disagree about the amount of child support, and a judge will need to decide since we both think that we're right."

After a decision on child support has been made, neither side should continue the legal battle. For the sake of the children, both the custodial and the non-custodial parent should accept the decision of the court. Ongoing legal fighting drains everyone, especially your children.

MEDICAL FEES

In addition to custody, visitation procedures, and child-support payments, divorce decrees often contain provisions relating to the child's medical care—including how decisions are made regarding recommended treatment and the payment for medical services. Frequently the non-custodial parent is to provide medical insurance for the child and pay for extraordinary health expenses not covered by insurance. The custodial parent is generally then required to pay for so-called "routine" medical expenses, which are often defined in terms of a fixed sum of money to be paid for each medical occurrence. For example, the first $25 may be deemed to be routine expenses. The agreements virtually always provide that the non-custodial parent is to be consulted prior to the administration of any medical treatment, except when the child's life might be imperiled by delay. This certainly sounds fair and straightforward.

Problems usually arise when either parent does not follow the terms of the decree, assuming the right to ignore or misinterpret the guidelines. For example, if a child is to have elective surgery—say the removal of moles, a nonemergency appendectomy, or any cosmetic surgery—some custodial parents assume that they have the authority to schedule the surgery without including the non-custodial parent in the process and that by "informing" the parent of the surgery they have complied with the terms of the decree. Merely informing the non-custodial parent of planned surgery does not meet the requirements of "prior consultation," which implies being involved in the decision-making process.

Non-custodial parents can cause conflict over medical procedures when they decide the custodial parent is taking the child to the doctors too often and arbitrarily decide not to pay for the services.

In each of these examples, parents tend to become very embroiled and angry. Children are often exposed to these disagreements and become worried and upset. Have they caused this problem by being ill? This is an unfair burden for a child, and teenagers especially might be extremely vulnerable to feeling guilty for something that is beyond their control. In medical expenses above all else, follow the procedures in your divorce decree, respect your former spouse as an interested, caring parent, and relinquish the need to decide and control. For the sake of your children, try co-parenting.

REPORT CARDS

An issue over which divorced parents sometimes clash is the non-custodial parent's right to have a copy of the child's report card. Many school districts send only one report card home, to the custodial parent. If divorced parents cooperate in co-parenting, the custodial parent simply makes a photocopy of the report card and sends it to the other parent. If the custodial parent is uncooperative and wants to exercise control, however, he or she may refuse to send a copy of the report card and refuse to give the school permission to release any information to the non-custodial parent.

School administrators should be encouraged to institute policies and procedures that will ensure that both parents receive copies of the report cards and other important school information. School personnel are justifiably leery of involvement in the legal conflict between parents, but if school boards, in conjunction with their legal counsel, would begin to endorse the rights of both parents to parent, it would contribute to the elimination of several areas of conflicts between parents. In addition, it would be an acknowledgment of the existence of many divorced families by the schools. (In many states, a child's school records are available to either parent—irrespective of which parent has been awarded custody in a divorce.)

105

SUGGESTIONS FOR CUSTODIAL PARENTS

1. Your child needs to have consistent, stress-free visitations with the other parent.

You have no power to control what happens when your child spends time with the other parent. Your attitude toward these visits, however, both before your adolescent goes and after he or she returns, can influence the emotional tone of the visits. If your former spouse is thirty minutes late you can take off in the car with your teenager to "show him that he can't push us around," or you can wait patiently and when your former spouse does show up, send your child off with a hug, accepting the explanation that your former spouse was tied up in a traffic jam. (If a pattern develops in which your former spouse is being truly and objectively irresponsible, deal directly with him or her—but not when your son or daughter is around.)

If you have developed the habit of trying to undermine and interfere with visitations, it is *you* who are creating stress for your teenagers. You can buy tickets for a special concert on your former spouse's weekend with the children, knowing it will cause problems; or you can plan such special outings only for those weekends you have your children with you. You can take your vacation at exactly the same time as your former spouse, or you can work to coordinate summer vacations for the maximum benefit of your children.

Teenagers hear the two of you arguing on the phone. They observes you slamming the door or changing plans at the last minute. The message you send them is "I hate your dad (or your mom)." They will only be hurt by such behavior and will withdraw from being honest with you. They will begin to tell you only what you want to hear or will become openly angry at you. Neither of these reactions is very productive for them or for you.

A final note to custodial parents: You and your former spouse have both had to make adjustments to accommodate visitations, and so will your teenager. Being a child from a divorced family is *not* like being a child from an intact family. It is important for children to recognize and accept their responsibility for communicating their needs and desires to the non-custodial parent. Learning to express feelings, ideas, and plans to the non-custodial parent will not only help your teenager develop an adult relationship with that parent but will also prepare him or her for communicating needs and desires to others.

2. You cannot force the other parent to exercise visitation rights.

In most instances, the non-custodial parent wants very much to maintain a relationship with his or her children. There are some cases, however, in which a parent deserts the family or in which a parent will not or cannot maintain contact with the children. This lack of contact may be the result of a number of factors: progressive alcoholism, guilt over the divorce, or the inability to really care for another person. The tensions and problems of the teenage years may even produce a situation (hopefully temporary) in which the non-custodial parent decides that he or she can no longer "handle" a relationship with a particular adolescent. If that has happened to your teenager, it may be very sad for both of you, especially since you know how important it is for your child to know and care for the other parent. In spite of your feelings there is *nothing* you can do to change your former spouse, and you certainly cannot force him or her to see the child.

You *can* answer your teen's questions honestly and tell him or her about the other parent. Share how you met, why you loved each other, and why you believe visitations are not occurring. This knowledge might help your adolescent child accept the parental rejection, and it will also reassure them that the rejection did not come about because they were "bad" or "unlovable" or a "juvenile delinquent."

SUGGESTIONS FOR NON-CUSTODIAL PARENTS

1. Your teenager needs your consistent attention and concern.

You are now in the difficult position of having an adolescent that needs you but does not live with you. It is probably a position you do not feel too happy about. Some non-custodial parents, experiencing so much pain in seeing their child only occasionally and in watching their relationship becoming fragmented, stop visiting with the child altogether. This can have disastrous consequences for a child—perhaps especially for a teenager. It is extremely important for the healthy development of adolescents that if at all possible they relate to both parents on a regular, dependable basis. The fact that the effort to relate with your children is more difficult after a divorce is not an acceptable excuse for not filling this basic need.

It is important that you, as the non-custodial parent, establish a consistent way to maintain contact with your teenager. When and how often you see your child may fluctuate depending on your son's or daughter's interests and needs. Perhaps during the swimming season you will see your son several times a week because you yourself are a swimmer and meet him several times a week for a workout. Or your daughter may get a part-time job after school and on weekends that limits the amount of time she can spend at your house for many months. You have commitments yourself, and it may be impossible always to be available to spend time with your teenager when he or she is free. As with younger children, however, with teens a parent needs to be willing to assume the majority of responsibility in facilitating visitations.

One good way to keep contact with your adolescent is to call at a mutually convenient time each week. Use this opportunity to share what is happening in each of your lives and to discuss and finalize upcoming plans to get together. If your teenager can commit to a regular visitation schedule, this will be easier for everyone, but realize that this is seldom possible with adolescents.

Most non-custodial parents are fathers. A father's input into his child's life is important at every age, but contact with him is especially important during the teenage years. Teenage boys need to relate to an adult male for their own identity formation, and girls too need the support and admiration of their fathers. Recent research has shown that adolescents who have a positive relationship with their fathers have better self-esteem and academic success.

There may be times when making the effort to keep in touch with your adolescent children seems like too much effort. Perhaps your former spouse makes arranging visitations very difficult, or the last time you were with your child you felt the child seemed bored, or your new girlfriend (boyfriend) or spouse does not like sharing you with your teenager. In spite of these or a myriad of other reasons, please go ahead with the visits as planned. Keep at it; you will realize much later how important it is.

2. Don't expect too much immediate gratification from your children.

Non-custodial parents sometimes make the mistake of expecting too much emotional support and recognition from their children. They are then disappointed when they feel their child has let them down. An adolescent's world is often self-centered and peer-oriented. Your fifteen-year-old daughter, for example, may be much happier on Saturday afternoon to get a call from her boyfriend than from her dad. Your eighteen-year-old son may say "no" to playing golf with his mom on Saturday morning but energetically go out to play basketball with his friends that same day.

Your birthday or Father's (Mother's) Day may go unnoticed. Do not take this personally. Remember, your adolescent is in many ways still a child who needs you to model caring, responsible behavior—whether you get the "strokes" you need or not. Keep sending cards and presents and get-well notes to your teenager. You are setting an example of how to care for someone when they are far away. This is an important lesson for your child to learn: that you can think about, care for, and love another person even if you don't live with them. As your adolescent matures and internalizes such caring behavior, you may someday find that your son goes out and selects a special Christmas gift for you or your daughter calls you up and invites you out to lunch. Then all your years of faithfulness will be repaid.

A non-custodial parent must put a lot of energy into the long range goal of the development of an emotionally healthy child and the creation of a positive, lifelong parent-child relationship. Considerable time and thoughtfulness is required of you now, and much of the payoff will not come for a few years. Of course there are many joys you will experience in spending time with your adolescent, but the most important satisfaction you will have is in knowing you have contributed substantially to your child's development.

CO-PARENTING

I cannot emphasize enough that teenagers need to know and be cared for by both parents, if at all possible. Children want to love and respect each of their parents. Understanding and applying this principle will do more to help your teenager facilitate a healthy adjustment to your divorce than *anything* else you can do. You can probably think of a dozen reasons why your former spouse does not deserve to be respected and liked—look at the way he or she treated you! The less you push this view on your adolescent, however, the better able he or she will be to form an independent evaluation of the other parent. If your former spouse really has despicable characteristics, your child will eventually learn about them firsthand and therefore will be less likely to blame you for them.

To have a successful co-parenting relationship, one that is healthy for the children, each parent must allow the other the freedom to parent in his or her own way. You should interfere or raise objections to what the other parent is doing *only* if your child's physical or emotional well-being is threatened. If your child is being left alone for long periods, abused in some way, or exposed to sex, drugs, or alcohol in a totally inappropriate way, then deal with that specific situation legally, under the provisions of the divorce decree. Otherwise, you must look the other way while your child is with your former spouse and hope that your values will be transmitted to your child through your words and actions while you are together.

In most post-divorce squabbles, the child's welfare is not being truly threatened—except from the stress engendered by being involved in ongoing bitter parental conflicts. If a child sleeps in a sleeping bag for a weekend or eats peanut butter for dinner, his or her safety is not jeopardized. If a child misses church or stays up until midnight on Saturday night, his or her future is not at risk. If a child is required to dress up (or down) when visiting the other parent, it will cause no permanent damage. If children occasionally have to miss an extended-family party because they are with their other parent, no one is going to die. These examples may include some practices of which you do not approve; it is certainly all right not to approve or like what the other parent does. You are probably divorced *because* you didn't agree on many issues and ideas. You do *not*, however, have a right to try to control what your child does with the other parent. In divorce, both parents lose some control of parenting. If you can accept this fact, you will create a better emotional atmosphere for both yourself and your children.

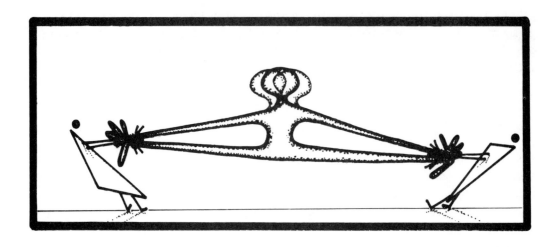

EXERCISE 7
How Would You Feel?

FOR YOU

Choose a time when you can be quiet and can count on not being disturbed for thirty minutes. Sit in a comfortable chair and close your eyes. Let go of thought of your busy life; relax.

Now remember what your life was like when you were the same age as your adolescent. Where did you live? (Picture it.) What was school like, who were your friends, what was your family like, how did you get along with your mother, your father?

Imagine what it would have been like if your parents had divorced when you were that age. (Perhaps they really did!) Who would you want to live with? Why? What type of visitation schedule would have been best for you?

Now think how this arrangement would have affected each of your parents. Perhaps they were so happy you can't imagine them getting divorced. Or perhaps they were so unhappy you can't understand why they didn't. Push yourself. Really try to do this exercise. What do you remember about being a teenager? How would a parental divorce have affected you at that time? How would it have affected your relationship with each parent?

After you have completed this exercise, share your memories and insights with a close trusted friend, minister, or counselor who also knows your teenage child. Discuss how you think that your son or daughter might be feeling right now, especially in terms of visitation and custody rights. Resolve what changes, if any, you plan to make and ask your friend to check up on you in a month to see if you have done them. (If you feel uncomfortable sharing your thoughts with another, perhaps you can write them in a journal or a letter and review them in a month.)

GENE'S EXAMPLE

Gene, a forty-nine-year-old engineer, shared his reactions with his parish priest. He recalled how hectic and fun—yet how confusing—it had been to be his son Larry's age, fifteen. He remembered the brick home he had lived in with his parents and three siblings and felt a sadness, a kind of melancholia, for a time past that could never be recaptured.

Gene realized that the idea of his parents divorcing at that time would have made him physically ill. He knew without hesitation that if it had happened he would have chosen to live with his mother. Gene related to the priest how his father had drunk heavily and the family was often tense wondering how it would be when Dad came home. His mother, on the other hand, was very involved with all the children and was really the heart of the family. Gene knew that if his parents had divorced when he was fifteen, he would seldom have wanted to be with his father and did not think his father would have had the emotional strength and insight to work at their relationship. He feared that his father's drinking would have increased if he and his mother had divorced, perhaps resulting in his father's early death. (In fact, Gene's father is still alive, in good health, and they now have a fairly good relationship.)

Gene was saddened by this realization. It made him aware that family relationship can be fragile—especially during a person's teen years—and that family members need to work at staying connected.

Gene then applied his thoughts to his relationship with his own son, Larry. Gene was not a drinker, as his father had been, but he had worked long hours when Larry was little and he still used work as an excuse to stay aloof from his son. Gene wondered if perhaps Larry felt the same way about him as he would have felt about his own father at Larry's age. Maybe Larry's lack of desire to be with Gene was a defense mechanism to prevent himself from being hurt. This made Gene feel sad, too, but he made a commitment to the priest that he would remain patient and work to establish a better relationship with his son. He made an appointment with the priest for a month later to discuss his progress on his resolution.

EXERCISE FOR AGES 12-14

Bake your teenager's favorite dessert. (Okay, get it from the bakery if you must.) This goodie will be the reward for your child completing this exercise.

111

After dinner, but before dessert, ask you son or daughter to complete the following:

For the Non-Custodial Parent:

For fun and to help me learn about this new way of being a family:

1. What are some things you like to do when you come to visit?
   a.
   b.
   c.

2. Is there anything I could change about our visits?

3. Overall, how do you think we are doing?

1	2	3	4	5	6	7	8	9	10
Awful					Okay				Great

For the Custodial Parent:

For fun and to help me learn about this new way of being a family:

1. What are some things we can do to have fun?
   a.
   b.
   c.

2. Is there anything I could do to make your visits with Mom (or Dad) easier?

3. Overall, how do you think we are doing?

1	2	3	4	5	6	7	8	9	10
Awful					Okay				Great

Have fun with this approach. It is *not* a serious research project. It should take your child only a minute to complete, and you can serve the dessert while he or she writes. As you eat the dessert, you can talk about the answers and what they mean.

EXERCISE FOR AGES 15-18

1. If you have a creative, expressive teen, purchase a small notebook and decorate the cover with the picture of your new family. Title the book "Reflections on Our Family." Give this to your son or daughter to use as a journal. He or she can write reflections, reactions, poetry, prose, or even insert clippings from newspapers and magazines. This journal is to be a private vessel, so promise your child that you will never read any of the entries unless asked.

2. If your child would be unwilling or unlikely to use a journal, plan an activity to do together. Let your teen decide—a quick trip to the ice-cream parlor or a Saturday afternoon at a ball game. Sometime during your outing ask your son or daughter how he or she is feeling about the amount and quality of time being spent with each parent. Carefully listen to the response. If there is some unhappiness expressed, schedule a time to talk about it at length—then go back to enjoying your time together.

TABLE TOPICS

1. Does anyone know of a family that is divorced that has the perfect visitation (or custody) arrangement? How does it work and why is it so good?
2. Given the fact that yours is a family of divorced parents, what would be the ideal way to plan the summer?
3. How are we doing financially? What are some things that we might do to spend less and/or bring in some more money?

CHAPTER 8

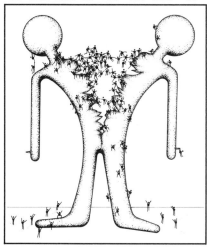

"EXTENDED" FAMILY RELATIONSHIPS

"Simon, how many tickets do you get for graduation?"

Simon's mother, Josephine

"Four."

Simon, an eighteen-year-old

"Well, who is going? I certainly don't want your father's new girlfriend there, and you know Nanie and Granddad are looking forward to seeing you graduate."

Josephine

Adjusting to divorce would be difficult enough if there were only the divorcing parents and their children to consider. Most families—including divorcing families—do not exist in a vacuum, however. There are family traditions that have been built over the years and now must be adapted or changed. There are usually relatives and other significant people who have close relationships with the parents and children. Reaction to the divorce by others close to the family may affect the post-divorce adjustment of all family members.

Family celebrations and relationships with grandparents, aunts, uncles, cousins, and adult family friends may become unclear and strained after a divorce. Extended family members frequently agonize over their problems in interacting with a divorced family. Likewise, after a divorce both parents and children may not know how to act toward relatives, former friends, and in-laws or how to celebrate significant events and holidays.

With a little bit of work, however, family celebrations and those who were important to you and your teenage children before the divorce may continue to be supportive resources and loving relationships.

GUIDELINES FOR FAMILY CELEBRATIONS

These guideline may help you when thinking about future family events: holidays, vacations, birthdays, weddings, graduations.

1. Both parents, regardless of who wanted the divorce, have a right to celebrate holidays and special events with their children.

Despite the circumstances of the divorce, both parents will remain the natural parents of a child for the rest of their lives. They deserve the right to celebrate important events with their children without interference from their former spouse.

2. Each parent must be flexible in timing their celebrations.

If it is the needs of the children that are truly to be met, then both parents must be willing to compromise on how this is to be accomplished. It is usually not possible for divorced parents to celebrate events together (although some successfully manage joint celebrations such as weddings or graduations).

3. The needs and rights of grandparents, aunts, uncles, and friends come after the rights of parents.

The bond between child and natural parent is very strong. This is true even in cases where there is little or no contact over a long period of time. Most other people, if they have the interest of the children at heart, will understand the importance of them maintaining a relationship with both their parents if at all possible.

4. Each parent needs to take responsibility for personally arranging celebrations with their adolescent children.

Teenagers often have strong ideas about what they want to do and often want to have input in any arrangements that affect them. If a parent discusses plans directly with the child, many disagreements and much confusion can be avoided. It is *not* a good idea for one parent to try to arrange celebrations for his or her former spouse and their children.

116

5. **Family celebrations after a divorce will never be the same as they were before the divorce.**

This seems obvious, but it is amazing how many divorced families try to pretend that "nothing has changed." Changes in family celebrations must be accepted gracefully, even though there may be some resentment—especially on the part of teenagers—-for the need to make adjustments. Those families that succeed in this transition realize that they must create a new life with new traditions.

HIGH SCHOOL GRADUATION

For many teenagers, high school graduation is a major event, one that marks the end of childhood and the beginning of being an adult. Adolescents usually approach graduation with mixed emotions. They look forward to the end of classes or the hated rules that they now consider "childish." Some favorite teachers are promised return visits, others are turned into myths of horror. A week or two before graduation, the senior prom is held in most schools. This event focuses the attention of the soon-to-graduate seniors on such details as special clothes, where to go after the prom, and who drives. The attention given the prom often allows the high school senior to slip closer toward graduation without really noticing.

Despite their show of bravado, however, most eighteen-year-olds are worried about their future. Those entering the work force are concerned about earning enough money to be considered an adult (which means being able to support a car, a social life, and eventually an apartment). Those going on to college worry about choosing the right school and the right major and how to pay for it all.

For both groups, the even bigger question is: "Will I be able to make it on my own?" Most high school students do not share these concerns with even their best friends, but beneath the "senior bravado" there lurks considerable doubt, fear, and anxiety.

Enter now a set of divorced parents fighting over who will attend the graduation ceremony and when various parties and celebrations will take place so that relatives and friends on both "sides" can participate. Simon's parent, Josephine and Bill, turned their son's graduation into a nightmare.

Josephine and Bill had separated at the end of Simon's junior year in high school. The wife had discovered that her husband was having an affair with a woman whom he continued to date after the divorce. Josephine was bitter and devastated, and the divorce was bitter and destructive.

Simon had withdrawn from both his parents, spending long hours at track practice, with his girlfriend, and at his job at a fast food restaurant. This withdrawal was actually very healthy for Simon, because he needed to protect his own emotional health and because there was really nothing that he could do to solve his parents' hatred for each other. Because of his silence on the matter, however, Simon told no one how he felt about the divorce and the battles between his mother and father.

When Josephine asked Simon who should get the four graduation tickets he had been allotted, he responded typically: "Do whatever you want, Mom. I don't care." So that is what Josephine did. She invited her own parents, Nanie and Granddad, and her brother Alfred, who was Simon's godfather. She also planned a large party after the graduation, inviting all her relatives and family friends.

Bill waited for Simon to invite him to the graduation. The invitation never came because of Simon's passivity regarding his parents and the distractions of finishing high school. Finally, three days before the graduation ceremony, Bill called Josephine and asked if there was a ticket for him. Josephine replied frostily that they were all used, that her parents had already arrived from out of town and that her brother, "a good role model," would also be attending. Josephine never told Simon that his father had called.

Bill was furious. He called the high school and the principal assured him that there were extra tickets. He asked Bill to stop by the office and he would personally see to it that Bill could attend his son's graduation. Bill, however, never picked up the ticket. He allowed his anger at his former wife to interfere with his showing support for his son.

During the ceremony, Simon looked for his father. While he had told his mother that he didn't care and had failed to call to invite his father, Simon was sure that his father would not miss the most important day of his life. When his father did not show up, another door to Simon's heart slammed shut. Simon has not talked to his father since the graduation.

RELATIONSHIPS WITH OTHERS

Although the immediate family—the divorcing parents and their children—are most affected by divorce, extended family members and close friends are also involved. The degree to which your divorce may have an impact on others will depend on several factors.

1. Their attachment and involvement with the family prior to divorce.

Some extended families and friends are actively involved in each other's lives. Birthdays, holidays, and even Sunday dinners are frequently shared. Grandparents babysit, aunts and uncles arrange weekend overnights for their nephews and nieces, a friend picks up a prescription for a sick baby or shares a secret recipe for potato salad. Other families have much less ongoing contact.

118

This may be because members live miles apart, because the family is small, or because the family never developed the expectation of providing mutual life support for others.

If either branch of your children's extended family or friends were actively involved with your pre-divorce family, then the divorce may be especially problematic for them. Each spouse may want his or her side to sever ties with the other. "Be loyal to me!" Parents, sisters and brothers, friends may want to support their "own," yet at the same time truly love and care for the other spouse and certainly for the children. The divorce creates a loss for these people as surely as it creates a loss for the divorcing family itself. They worry about how to act, what to say, whom to talk to, how to function.

2. Their degree of hostile involvement in the divorce process.

Some divorces become unfortunately embittered, drawn-out battles stretching over years. They may include many trips to the attorney, hurried court appearances, scenes in the courthouse corridor, police reports, religious annulment proceedings, and horrendous attorney fees. Extended family and friends often become involved in these occurrences—sometimes willingly, most times against their better judgment. The intensity of this fighting often results in permanently broken relationships among the adults, which is often carried over to or taken out on the children.

It would be wonderful if all such hostile divorces could be avoided. There are, however, people who obsessively pursue their legal battles at the expense of themselves, their children, and their families and friends. If you were married to such a person, you may need emotional and financial support from your extended family and friends. They will feel hurt and angry for you. This is a natural response to your suffering and will carry over to their feelings for your former spouse. The reverse may be true of your relationships with your former spouse's extended family.

3. The amount of contact desired on both sides.

Just as extended families and friends develop many variations in the amount of actual interaction and expressed closeness, so too will they have differing preferences for how much involvement they desire after divorce. Even if you encourage your former spouse's parents to remain involved in your children's lives, for example, they may decide for any number of reasons that they want to have minimal or no contact. On the other hand, perhaps your former spouse's best friend wants more contact with your children than you feel comfortable with.

It is important not to personalize these reactions. There are some people who simply are not flexible enough to accommodate the reality of divorce, and others feel that it should not affect their relationships at all. The bottom line, however, is that your teenagers need the support, caring, and interest of many adults in their lives. You and your former spouse will always play the most important roles, but it is extremely helpful if other adults can play a part.

(Another crucial factor, of course, is how much and what type of contact your adolescent wants with others. Teenagers often feel that no one asks them for their ideas or takes them seriously. They usually prefer spending much of their time with peers and may even dread attending family events. Fortunately, this is a time-limited, developmental phase. In just a few years, when they are in their twenties, these very same teenagers may patiently visit a grandparent in a nursing home or plan a big surprise birthday party for a parent. So encourage your teen to attend some family celebrations, but allow him or her to limit the time spent at such events or allow a teenage friend to come along.)

4. The degree to which an extended family member personalizes your divorce.

Some extended family members or friends tend to "personalize," or take personally, another's divorce. For example, a mother may say to her adult son, "How could you do this to your father and me?" The son, of course, is bewildered and hurt. The divorce is happening to him. He is the one missing his children, financially strapped with lawyer's fees and child support, trying to adjust to apartment living. Yet now his mother is trying to make him feel responsible for her feelings as well.

Such personalization may cause that person to pull back from seeing you or your spouse or even your children. It may help to face the issue directly: "Mother, I know you wish Jane and I had not divorced. I do, too. However, we did not do this to hurt you and Dad. My being divorced does not mean you and Dad didn't bring me up right. We divorced because our marriage was not working. I need you and the kids need you and maybe even Jane needs you." Time passing may also help depersonalize the divorce. A year or two later, what now seems so devastating may be manageable.

5. The degree to which the divorce is perceived as a moral, religious, or social stigma.

People view divorce through many different lenses. Some feel strongly that it is a moral and religious flaw or error, even a sin. Others agree with this view but their feelings are not so intense. Still others believe that divorce is a sad, unfortunate, hurtful experience but that individuals who divorce are not bad or immoral social misfits. If your extended family and friends are judgmental on this issue, you may be feeling unacceptable and isolated. You may be missing important support and understanding at a time when you really need it. It is probably better to look elsewhere for your support than to try to change their beliefs.

Your adolescent will probably be perceptive enough to pick up on how extended family members are responding to the divorce. If negative feelings exist, take time to explain to your child what you believe is happening. "I'm sure you have noticed that Aunt Millie rarely calls anymore. She believes that your dad and I have committed a sin by divorcing and feels uncomfortable talking with me. I wish she could be more understanding, but you know Dad and I are decent people who try to live honest, caring lives. I hope in time Aunt Millie will understand why we got divorced, but right now we probably won't see her very often."

GRANDPARENTS

After Anna and Alan separated, his mother stopped calling Anna. Anna called once or twice after the separation but when she picked up on the older woman's uneasiness, she gave up. Anna thought perhaps Alan's parents were angry and were blaming her for the divorce. She felt badly about the loss of contact with her former in-laws, for her own parents lived 1200 miles away. Anna felt even worse for her in-laws than she did for herself. The retired couple had enjoyed her daughter Michelle ever since her birth seventeen years ago, and now they seldom saw her.

With Anna's permission, a counselor she was seeing phoned Alan and asked if he would be willing to bring his parents to a session to talk about whether they would like to see more of Michelle. He agreed to ask them. His parents were leery of counselors, and so it was with some reluctance that they agreed to meet.

Alan's parents are like many grandparents. They grew up in an era in which divorce was uncommon. Both are devout Catholics and were having a very difficult time accepting the fact that their oldest son was divorced. It became clear that they were as uneasy with their own son, Alan, as they were with Anna. They felt ashamed of having a divorce in the family. They had not even told some relatives that Alan and Anna were divorced. They felt that their son's divorce somehow reflected on the kind of parents they had been. Had they raised Alan wrong?

The counselor acknowledged their concerns and helped them understand that Alan and Anna's divorce was a decision made by two responsible adults and that they had not raised a bad son. They saw how Alan was meeting his financial responsibilities to Anna and Michelle and how he faithfully spent time with his daughter. Alan was also willing to begin the official church annulment process, which seemed to relieve his mother. They were urged to discuss some of their concerns with a priest they admired and respected. By this time in the conversation, the elder couple was more relaxed and began talking about Michelle. They too missed seeing her and Anna, and when told that Anna and Michelle missed them too the grandfather began to cry. In no time at all a plan was worked out for Michelle to drive over to her grandparents' house about once a month for dinner. If she didn't have other plans, Michelle would sleep over with her grandparents, attend Mass with them, go out for Sunday brunch, and then come home. Anna agreed to let Michelle have the family car for these special outings. The grandparents were happy to be given "official" permission to continue a relationship with Michelle and Anna that did not always have to include Alan, and Michelle was pleased to see her grandparents alone and to be trusted to make the arrangements herself.

This particular story had a happy ending, but in many instances the results are not as happy. Some divorced people do not like their former in-laws, and some even blame them for the divorce. Some grandparents become so embroiled in the divorce process that they even become embittered toward their own grandchildren.

There are no socially accepted rules for how parents should act when their adult children divorce. Some divorce decrees include visitation rights of grandparents, although most do not. If their divorced son or daughter does not arrange for them to have contact, these unhappy victims of the divorce often feel they have no effective means to maintain a relationship with their grandchildren. Many grandparents simply don't know what to do. They feel stigmatized, confused, and embarrassed. As a result, they may withdraw from the family.

If at all possible, teenagers need to know (or know about) their grandparents in order to have a real sense of their identity and "roots." When two people divorce, they are no longer legally connected to each other. Their children, however, will always be biologically, legally, and socially tied to both sides of their heritage.

The importance of grandparents to grandchildren has begun to be recognized by the legal community in the granting of legal visitation rights to grandparents. The State of Illinois divorce act, for example, provides that grandparents may petition the court and secure an order granting them the right to visitation with their grandchildren. The action by the legislature is in response to the important role that grandparents can play in the welfare of the children. In a number of cases the custody of the children has even been awarded to the grandparents.

You do not need to take on all the responsibility for maintaining your teenager's relationship with your ex-spouse's parents. You are younger and more flexible than the grandparents, however, and your actions might encourage initial contacts. Here are some suggestions for promoting a good post-divorce relationship:

- Communicate directly with your former in-laws. Tell them you hope they will continue to see the children. Work out a plan that is mutually agreeable.
- Do not discuss the divorce or their son or daughter's behavior, as this may cause tension. Do *not* try to get them on your side, for most parents will support their own child. Any attempts at discrediting their child will only result in tension between you and the grandparents.
- Encourage your children to send cards to their grandparents at holidays and birthdays. Teenagers are capable of doing this on their own, but they may need your help. (This is an excellent issue on which to start teaching teens responsibility. Perhaps giving them a calendar with all the family dates on it would be an appropriate way to start.)
- If your former in-laws live a long distance away, give permission to your adolescent children to call occasionally. Perhaps you too could get on the phone when they do, telling the grandparents about what the children are doing.
- Invite the grandparents to school occasions, ball games, and dance recitals. Send school pictures; grandparents love those pictures!

Not only your parents-in-law will have a problem with the divorce. What about your own parents? They may also have some difficulty in understanding and accepting your divorce. Tell your parents exactly what you and your children need from them. For example, you might say, "Dad and Mom, I know you don't really approve of our getting a divorce, but I hope you won't be angry at me and the children about it. Please understand that I am working very hard and trying to take care of the children alone. Sometimes I may just need to complain a little. It doesn't mean you have to solve my problems. Dad, it would really help me out if you could go with Brad to look at a used car he wants to buy. I know nothing about cars, and he has his heart set on buying 'wheels' before school starts."

Of course, asking for what you need doesn't guarantee that you will always get it. When grandparents (your parents) are specifically asked for support, however, they almost always come through for their child and grandchildren if they possibly can.

In the traumatic time of divorce, both adults and children need the love, support, and interest of people who care for them. Grandparents often have time and resources to give. It is a nice exchange.

During one in-service workshop for approximately 150 teachers, I asked them to think of a child from a single parent home who was well-adjusted and doing well in school. Then I asked them to think about what it was about that child that seemed to contribute to this positive adjustment. One of the most important factors cited by the teachers was the involvement and support of at least one grandparent.

OTHER RELATIVES

If the status and role of grandparents in divorce is undefined and fuzzy, the role and rights of other relatives is non-existent. Prior to the divorce, your family may have frequently celebrated holidays with your wife's side of the family. She has several brothers and sisters, all married, several with children. At these occasions the little cousins would roughhouse or ride bikes while the older children watched videos and played complicated card games. A favorite sister or brother was selected to be your child's godmother or godfather. Aunt and Uncle always sent special birthday and Christmas gifts to the children. This family ritual continued for the fifteen years you had been married.

Now comes the divorce. What should you do about these people who have been so dear to you and your children? You know your former spouse will continue to see his or her relatives and that your children will see their aunts, uncles, and cousins when they are with him or her. What about you? You really liked some of your spouse's relatives. Should you send cards at holidays, invite them to your home, send gifts to your nieces and nephews, make attempts to stay in touch?

There are no easy answers to these questions. The answers depend on the nature of your relationship with the extended family before the divorce, how much damage the divorce process did to those relationships, and the attitudes and wishes of the extended family.

If you had a genuine, warm, and caring relationship with your former spouse's brothers and sisters, and if during the divorce they managed not to become embroiled in any major disagreements, then perhaps now you can cultivate and maintain a separate, but meaningful, relationship with them. You must remember, however, that they are your former spouse's relatives. If he or she is attempting to place emotional and physical distance between the two of you, then in all likelihood you will not be invited to extended family functions. Do not take this personally. Understand the delicate position of your former relatives.

What you can do is create some new events to share. Perhaps when you take your teenagers out for pizza a favorite aunt and uncle can be invited, or maybe a close cousin can be asked to share a weekend with your son or daughter. Send appropriate remembrances of birthdays and special events. This will be an acknowledgment of your feelings and will encourage building ongoing, supportive relationships for you and your child.

Aunts and uncles and cousins may not know what role they have in this new, split family. Like grandparents, they may withdraw and wait until you make a move by phoning or planning a get-together. Do not interpret the lack of initiative on their part as not caring. Think about the type of new relationship you want to structure and then reach out to them.

Creating a new family alignment may not be a real possibility for you. Perhaps you did not even like your former spouse's relatives prior to the divorce but tolerated them at family functions. They may have lived such a distance that you really never got to know them. During the divorce, your spouse may have involved them to such an extent that you still harbor angry, hurt feelings. If any of these situations closely reflects your circumstances, it is best to accept this reality and not try to force artificial, strained get-togethers.

You can, however, help your children immensely by not speaking negatively about their aunts, uncles, and cousins, and by understanding your teenager's need to have contact with and permission to enjoy extended families on both sides.

Bonnie, a divorced mother, has eight grown brothers and sisters all living within a ten-mile radius of her home. Bonnie's former husband Sid resented the closeness of the extended family when he and Bonnie were married, and as a result he never felt like he quite "fit in." During the divorce Bonnie's brothers and sisters were very supportive of her; they drove her to court, loaned her money, and took her and her children into their homes. This made Sid furious because he wanted Bonnie to need him so much that she would consider a reconciliation.

After the divorce, when the children went to visit their father, Sid would constantly run down Bonnie's brothers and sisters—the children's aunts and uncles. The children loved their aunts and uncles, and they also loved their father. The more Sid talked about the aunts and uncles, the more the children withdrew from their father, finally reaching the point where they no longer wanted to visit him.

Understand the need of your children to feel proud of all of their family members, your side and your former spouse's side. You do not have to share your child's feelings, but you must not attempt to force your child to mirror your feelings.

FAMILY FRIENDS

Your child's relationships with close adult family friends may also be affected by the divorce. Relationships may be lost or altered when your children move away from the family residence or when adult friends are primarily "Mom's" or primarily "Dad's." After the divorce, these people seldom see the child if the child lives with the parent who is not their close friend.

Although loss of contact with adult friends may not be as hurtful as the loss of contact with relatives, it still represents change and discontinuity. More important, adult friends can be important sources of support to teenagers. If there are adults who have been especially interested in your children, try to encourage the relationship to continue in some manner. For example, on Saturday afternoon when you visit the old neighborhood to see an elderly neighbor, take your teen with you. Or ask your son or daughter to drop off a book to your (or your former spouse's) good friend's home. These occasions help your adolescent maintain some of his or her first, although limited, adult friendships.

Over time, all relationships change. New friends are made, old ones fade away. For whatever reason, some adults may lose interest in your children. If during the first year or so after separation you can help your teenager maintain some contact with family friends, however, it will help foster a sense of security. Your teenager and adult friends alike may need a little encouragement from you to accomplish this.

My former husband was an only child, and both of his parents were dead by the time we had been married two years. Thus over time my family became his family, they loved him and he loved them. When we divorced after seventeen years of marriage, it was difficult for everyone to sort out what type of relationships should exist between my former spouse and my family. The relationships that have continued are based on the mutual respect and caring that had developed over the years. My former spouse corresponds directly with my extended family, remembering birthdays and Christmas. My father, who likes to call his own children, also calls my former husband just to chat about his job and fishing. When my mother was in failing health, my former husband took vacation time and flew from San Francisco to Florida to spend several days visiting her—this was seven years after our divorce! I find that not only do these contacts *not* bother me, but that I am very glad that they have continued for both my former husband's sake and that of our children.

So, although family ties change, they do not have to end. You do have a choice.

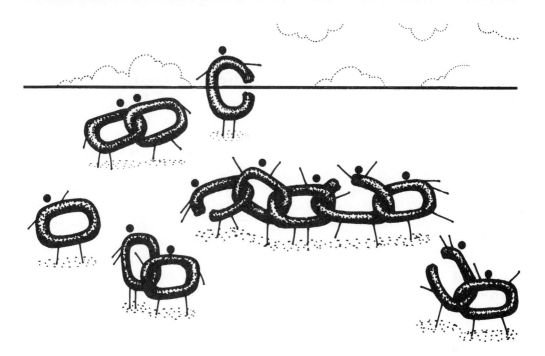

EXERCISE 8
Reconnecting the Broken Links

FOR YOU

Take out an 8½ × 11″ sheet of notebook paper. For a minute, just think of the interactions you have with members of both sides of your extended pre-divorce family. Now picture the person for whom your divorce has proven most difficult. Write down the name of that person with whom you wish to establish a better, more honest communication.

On the left side of the paper list why/how the divorce has created problems in this relationship. On the right side write any suggestions for improving the relationship. Finally, across the bottom, describe how the exercise affected you.

KATIE'S EXAMPLE

Person with whom the divorce has affected my relationship the most: my mother.

Why/How Affected	Suggestions for Improving
1. Mother always regarded the role of wife highly. Being a good wife to my father was her main adult life task. Therefore, she sees me as failing in the main thing she prepared me for.	1. Tell mother I understand she is disappointed and angry. Tell her I am disappointed and angry too, but I just could not stay married to Roger.

127

2. Mother knows it was I who filed for the divorce, that I was the one who finally gave up on the marriage. She seems angry with me.

3. Mother has always had difficulty expressing or understanding feelings. She seems unable to talk with me about the divorce. She is staying away from seeing me and the children.

2. Take mother to lunch, away from the home. Talk with her about how I think she has been such a good wife for Dad. Let her know I appreciate her values.

3. Let time elapse. Ask mother over or just stop by with the children more often. As she experiences that we are still the same people, she may relax and feel free to resume her frequent visits.

My reaction: I am shocked by how upset I felt doing this exercise. I realize that I will need to expend energy helping my mother adjust to my divorce—just when I need her to help me. Yet I love my mother and know she has a very difficult time adjusting to changes. I wish she were different, but I also realize that she is not going to change at her age.

Comment

Katie is a thirty-eight-year-old divorced mother of two teenagers. She had invested a lot of energy in helping her children adjust to the divorce. This exercise made her aware that not only they needed support, but so did her own mother—who was taking the divorce very badly.

When Katie started thinking about this exercise, she thought she would write about her sister-in-law who recently had written her a very nasty letter about hurting her brother (Katie's former husband). As she was reflecting, however, Katie suddenly pictured her mother and knew she needed to explore this relationship first. (Often there are several relationship that have been altered by the divorce. It may be too much emotional work to repair them all at one time. Do what you have the heart and energy for and put the rest off for another day.)

Katie realized that her mother was personalizing the divorce by feeling that she had somehow failed in her efforts to prepare Katie to be the perfect wife and mother. Yet because her mother had difficulty expressing or even understanding feelings, she wasn't even aware of this reaction. Instead, her mother was just withdrawing from both her daughter and her grandchildren. Katie decided that she would try to rebuild her mother's confidence in herself as a mother and continue to see her as often as possible, while giving her mother the time she needed to heal.

EXERCISE FOR AGES 12-14

On a piece of paper, write down "Thanksgiving," "Christmas," or "Hanukkah," and your teenager's birth date. Leave several lines under each heading. Ask your son or daughter to write how he or she would like to celebrate each event this year with each parent. Who else would they like to see included: grandparents, aunts, uncles, cousins, adult friends?

After the exercise is complete, read over the ideas together. Talk about any obvious difficulties you see with the plans and request permission to keep the suggestions. If appropriate, suggest that your child share the ideas with the other parent, maybe even taking it out and mailing it right away and stopping for a treat on the way home. Try to remember to incorporate as many of your teenager's suggestions as possible over the next year into your own family celebrations.

EXERCISE FOR AGES 15-18

Ask your child if there are any relatives or adult friends he or she would like to see and talk with—just for fun or because he or she cares for that person. Give your child permission to call (long-distance, if necessary) to talk with that person, or, if you live close enough, use the family car to stop by for a visit. (If the person chosen comes from your former spouse's side of the family or friends, try not to let your personal feelings intrude into the discussion.)

When the call or visit is complete, ask your teenager how it went and encourage him or her to continue the relationship. Perhaps suggest that your son or daughter invite that person over for dinner or to the next family event. In this way, you will be encouraging your teenager to begin taking adult responsibility for "relationship tending."

TABLE TOPICS

1. How will we remember birthdays, anniversaries, and special events on your former spouse's side of the family?
2. How do the children think their grandparents (on both sides) have adjusted to the divorce? (Let the children talk. You listen.)
3. What is friendship? Will the friends we have now be our friends ten years from now? How do we work to make sure that happens?

CHAPTER 9

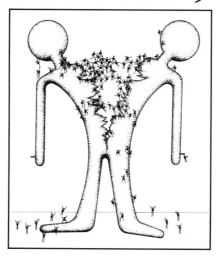

DATING AND REMARRIAGE

"Mom, if you marry Pete don't plan on me coming to the wedding!"

Allison, a fifteen-year-old

Betty, was surprised, mystified, and hurt by her daughter Allison's response to her announcement that she was planning to remarry that fall. Allison had always liked her mother's fiance, Pete, and Betty assumed he would be welcomed into the family by Allison and her thirteen-year-old brother Mack.

Betty and her former husband, Doug, had divorced three years ago. The first year had been rough, with both parents and children becoming upset very easily. The couple, however, had learned to communicate better—at least about their children—and things had calmed down considerably.

In year two, both parents had begun to develop a satisfying adult social life, and Doug had remarried about a year ago. Both teenage children seemed to accept his new wife. Betty had joined a single-parent's social organization to meet other single people, and this group helped fill the weekends when all her married friends were busy.

Betty had met Pete about fourteen months ago on her job. At first they went out only when Allison and Mack were with their father. As their relationship deepened, however, Betty began to include Pete in some of her family's functions. The couple had even included the teenagers on a week long vacation to a nearby lake, and everyone had seemed to hit it off well—especially Pete and Mack.

As Betty reflected on Allison's reaction to the wedding announcement, she remembered that during this vacation, Pete had spent much of the time fishing with Mack while Allison and Betty sunned on the pier and went shopping. Betty wondered if this had been their mistake. Perhaps Pete should have included Allison in more outings.

Since school had started last fall, Allison had been very busy with her friends—asking to stay overnight on Fridays and Saturdays at friends' houses and in general being away from home quite often. Betty considered this to be normal teenage behavior, but now she wondered if Allison was staying away to avoid Pete.

Betty did not know what to do. She knew Pete was a nice man and she felt fortunate to have a "second chance" at marriage. In fact, Betty felt very happy and in love for the first time in many years. Yet Betty did not want to do anything to hurt her two teenagers further. Life was becoming very complicated once again—just when Betty had thought the difficult days were behind her.

Betty and Pete consulted a family counselor, who scheduled several joint sessions with all four members of the new family-to-be. In these sessions, Allison revealed that she was upset because she didn't want another adult—Pete—setting rules for her. She also was very uncomfortable at the thought of running around the house in her nightgown with a "strange" man in the house.

Allison's concerns related to two areas in which many teenagers have difficulty: rules and sexuality. When a stepparent enters the family, these concerns can become magnified. Betty and Pete have decided to go ahead with their wedding, but they are now aware of at least two of the real concerns that were making Allison hesitate in welcoming the change. They have determined that Betty will continue to set the rules for the two teenagers and that everyone will be especially sensitive about questions of modesty. They also plan to continue monthly family sessions with the counselor for a few months.

Dating and especially remarriage require new levels of understanding, acceptance, and flexibility on the part of both divorced parents and their children. All children want parents to be available to them and fear that involvement in another relationship might interfere with that availability. Many children also harbor unrealistic hopes that their divorced parents will get back together, and dating and remarriage dash these hopes. For adolescents trying to master intimate relationships themselves, watching a parent struggle with the same issues can be especially difficult and unsettling.

DATING

After a marriage ends, most people eventually build a new social life—which often includes dating. Even people who do not, for religious reasons, contemplate remarriage as long as their former spouse is alive, recognize the value of interacting with members of the opposite sex.

Whether and how long before dating begins, and how many different dating partners a person has, varies tremendously. Some people prefer to wait to date until the divorce is final. For some people, it may take months, or even years, before they feel emotionally ready or have an opportunity to date. And some people begin seeing other people, or one special person, before their marriage is even legally dissolved. This may not be as outrageous as it seems. Once a couple separates, they often feel "divorced," but the legal proceedings stretch out over a number of months—or in some cases even years.

There will be considerable difference of opinion among divorced people about the right time and right way to begin dating. There is some danger in beginning to date too soon after a divorce. Most people need a period of "mourning" to get over the "death" of the old, intact family. Individuals are very vulnerable immediately after a separation, and premature serious dating can lead to getting remarried "on the rebound"—which could result in a second divorce. The "right" time to start dating is simply when you are emotionally open to new people and when someone you like becomes available.

There are two major factors for you to consider when thinking about how dating will affect your teenage children's lives: your own dating pattern and your attitude toward your former spouse's dating.

YOUR OWN DATING

If you begin to date, it is important that your teenagers not feel pushed aside or replaced. It may make you feel so good to court someone or be courted that you find yourself somewhat "high." When you feel this good it is very difficult to tell your new friend or friends that you need to stay home with your children several nights a week. You may even be tempted to stay home but have your date come over to your home.

Think about how this might feel to your teens. They have lost their intact family structure. Now they may feel you too will be lost, lost to a new love. Telling them, "Len is not trying to be your father, he is just my friend," will not alleviate their feeling that you may want or need Len more than you care for them.

By all means date Len. You don't have to marry him—or anyone else, for that matter! Go out, get dressed up, have fun. Introduce Len to your son and

133

daughter, include them—if they are available—in some of your outings together, even have him over to your house on occasion. But also plan time at home without Len. Continue to do things with your teens without Len; balance your time. They need you and need "special" time alone with you—not just day-to-day "necessary" time.

This balancing act may be difficult, but it is important in helping your children feel secure. If you have primary custody of your children and have free time only every other weekend, for example, you may feel it is unfair that your former spouse can go out every night. You already have so much responsibility and now must limit your dating while your former spouse has so much freedom! It is true this may not be exactly fair, but very little about divorce can be viewed as fair. Your former spouse may feel it is unfair that you get to make the major decisions about the children and that it is unfair that he or she cannot have custody. Each of you must live with and accept the reality and limits of the divorce.

People you date can have a positive influence on your children. They may help you feel better about yourself, feel happier. If you are happy, it will help your children feel happy. By getting to know other adult men or women, your teenagers may be exposed to new ideas and new experiences. If people you are dating genuinely like them, they can become other supportive relationships for them.

If your children do not like the person you date, or a person you date does not like your children, this can prove to be very upsetting. Perhaps they are jealous of each other, each wanting to control you. Adolescents have a more difficult time than younger children accepting stepparents. They have lived a much longer time than younger children in their original family and are often not sure they need or want another. Teenagers are also sometimes more difficult for a new person to get to know and love than a younger child. So there may be tension between your new adult friends and your adolescent children. If you are feeling conflicts and pressures over this issue, talk with a professional counselor a time or two to help you sort through what is happening. Both your children and your new love interest are important to you, but you must never let any of them begin to run your life. It is you who must decide how you will handle your choices and responsibilities.

YOUR FORMER SPOUSE'S DATING

You are not responsible for your former spouse's dating pattern, but rather for your *attitude* toward his or her dating. It is critical to understand and accept the fact that you cannot control who or how frequently your former spouse dates. If you will accept this fact you will feel much freer and happier and it will be much easier for your teenagers to deal with it in their own way.

You will certainly have feelings about your former spouse's caring for someone besides you. This is normal and understandable and part of the process of divorce. Be aware of these feelings and, if you can, share them with another adult. Longstanding relationships and feelings do not end or change the minute the judge signs the divorce decree. Yet, regardless of these feelings, it is very hurtful and damaging to lay them on your children.

When your former spouse begins dating or falls in love with someone else, it may stir up all sorts of feelings in you. You may experience jealousy toward the new person, anger at being replaced, sadness in realizing that the marriage is over, or fear that your children will like the new person more than they like you. Perhaps you might even feel happiness or relief that your former spouse is starting a new social life.

Feelings of jealousy, anger, sadness, and fear may be so intense that they strongly influence interactions between divorced parents when they relate to each other about their children. Divorced parents sometimes feel the only way they have any leverage with a former spouse about dating is by limiting access to the children, or by attempting to control visitations: "You can't have Marge to your apartment when the children are over!"

Parents confuse their teenagers by expressing their opinions about their former spouse's new friends: "Your mother has turned into a whore, sleeping at her boyfriend's house while you are with me," or "Your father's new girlfriend thinks she is so sophisticated! I will not have her taking you shopping for clothes," or "I forbid your mother's date to come to your graduation. If he does I will beat him to a pulp."

When the person you loved for many years—and possibly still do—chooses someone else, it is understandable that you have a strong response. For the sake of the children, however, it is important not to let these intense feelings be seen by them. Begin to let go of feelings of attachment (love or hate) for your former spouse.

You may not want to "let go" because that will confirm that the relationship as it was between you and your former spouse no longer exists. This can be painful, for it demonstrates that both of you will not only survive your divorce but must build a new life without each other. Perhaps this is something you really do not want. Some people remain bitterly attached to their former spouse years after the divorce. They say: "I can't help it. I just can't help how I feel." If you find this happening to you, consider talking with a professional counselor. As you master letting go you will discover that who your former spouse dates and what they do is no longer as important to you.

Adolescents are often dating too. So most teens understand the need to have someone who finds them attractive and wants to be with them. If you are overly critical of your former spouse's dating, your teenager may begin to question your motives and objectivity. In addition, your teenager may enjoy and gain from knowing people your former spouse dates. Allow your son or daughter this freedom, for—as with someone you date—your former spouse's new friend may be another person who really cares for your child.

SEX

One especially difficult issue for some is the question of extra-marital sex. If you are opposed to sex outside of marriage, it may be difficult to deal with the fact that your former spouse might be having sex with another with the knowledge of your children or sometimes even in the same house or apartment where they are staying. This may reflect an important difference in values and morality between you and your former spouse—perhaps one that was a major cause of your divorce.

Adolescents are especially sensitive and concerned about the sexuality of their parents. If you believe that your teenagers are upset by your former spouse's behavior, encourage them to talk with that parent directly (and as dispassionately as possible) about it or even enlist a third party to do so. Try to stay out of the matter if at all possible. If it is absolutely necessary for you to speak with your former spouse about the matter, suggest that the only issue you are concerned about is what is being communicated to the children. Ask your former spouse to consider more discretion when they are around. If this does not work, *drop the subject*. Nothing that you say or do is going to change the situation.

With your teenager, you are free to make a clear statement of your disapproval of such activity. Once this has been done, however, only your positive example and teaching has any hope of effectively transmitting your values regarding sexual activity to your children. Continual harping on this subject with either your former spouse or your teen will only leave you open to criticism for interference or ridicule for prudery. Your adolescent might turn you off on the entire subject of sex—just when they need your advice and concern the most.

If you are engaging in extra-marital sex yourself, remember that teenagers are easily influenced by your example. You may find yourself in the position of recommending that they "do as I say, not as I do." On the issue of your sexual behavior, discretion and common sense regarding the welfare of your children is imperative.

REMARRIAGE

As if managing the emotions and relationships created when divorced parents begin to date were not complicated enough, adjustment for parents and teenagers takes a new turn if and when either parent remarries. Remarriage seals the fate that there will be no parental reconciliation (although even children in their teens and twenties often have fantasies about reconciliation of their original family long after both parents have remarried).

Not only is the door of reality closed on reconciliation, but new people are brought into the teenagers' lives for whom they are supposed to have, or at least begin to have, a "family" feeling. Here is another major change—just like the divorce itself—when children feel that they have had no control over their own family structure.

If remarriage takes place within a year or two after the divorce, all children will still be in the process of adjusting. At the same time they are adjusting to the losses created by the divorce, they must also adjust to the entrance of a step-parent, sometimes bringing with him or her stepchildren, stepgrandparents, and even step-pets.

Some of the major problem areas for remarriages are disagreements about children. These do not need to become crises between you and your new spouse, but it is important to discuss together your values and beliefs about child-rearing prior to remarriage. All family members, old and new, must realize that they are members of a remarried family and that a remarried family is *not* like an original nuclear family. An acceptance of this "differentness" may remove a lot of pressure from everyone.

If you remarry, do not expect or encourage your teenagers to call your new spouse "Dad" or "Mom." Your children already have a set of parents—you and your former spouse—and will probably resent your trying to suggest otherwise. Allow the relationship between your children and your new spouse to develop naturally. In some instances, particularly where the biological parent emotionally or physically deserts a teenager, a close parent-child relationship may develop between the teen and the stepparent. Over time, he or she may choose to call your new spouse "Mom" or "Dad." That must be his or her choice, however. Do not try to force it in any way. Be sensitive to your child's feelings, and accept his or her ongoing loyalty to the other natural parent.

Recent research that explored children's adjustment to step-families found that adolescents have more difficulty accepting a stepparent than younger children. Teenagers have spent more time in their original family than younger children and thus may find it hard to accept a new person. Teenagers also do not like "a stranger" telling them what to do. To prevent problems on this score, it is best whenever possible for the biological parent to establish and enforce rules. The stepparent can still be supportive of his or her spouse's decisions and enforce "house" rules when the biological parent is not present.

Stepparents can add support and security to a single parent family, bringing to the family some additional time and energy and even money that may be very much needed. If you or your former spouse remarry, take some time to consider how this will affect your teenagers. Have family discussions and ask the teens for their input about how they would like the new family to function. Allow them to care for new family members—including members of your former spouse's family—but don't force feelings.

If both you and your former spouse remarry, your teenagers will belong to two separate remarried families. They will still and always will have, however, only one set of parents—you and your former spouse. Your original relationship will exist with your children forever.

EXERCISE 9
Bridging the New Chasms

FOR YOU

Choose one new social relationship that is causing you some discomfort. It could be your former husband's new girlfriend, the son of the person you are dating, or your former wife's new husband. Write the name of that person across the top of a piece of paper and under the name write your relationship to that person.

Form four columns across the page: "Feelings Toward (name of person)," "How They Affect Me," "How They Affect My Children," and "Possible Solutions." Decide which of the solutions you might begin to implement in the upcoming week.

EVE'S EXAMPLE

Kristine
Chuck's (My Former Husband's) Live-in Girlfriend

Feelings toward Kristine

1. Angry

2. Jealous

How They Affect Me

1. I loose control.

   I feel hot inside.

   I even feel sick.

2. I buy new clothes to compete with her.

   I find myself cutting down her work.

   I say sarcastic things to Chuck about her.

**How Affects Children
(Lucy, 18, Rosie, 14)**

1. They see me act hostile when they mention her name.

   They saw me slam down the phone when she called.

   They have heard me say sarcastic things to others about her.

2. They know I am not acting like myself.

   They see me as hypocritical, because I used to admire educated women.

   They are embarrassed.

3. Rosie is beginning to question my position on sexual abstinence before marriage.

Possible Solutions

1. Begin to accept the fact that Chuck left me by choice; Kristine did not make him leave me.

   Meditate on forgiveness—pray for calmness.

   Accept the fact that my girls like her.

2. Begin to know and like myself. (How do I do that?)

   Put energy into my own job.

   Keep quiet about Kristine.

3. Share with Rosie how I feel about sex before marriage. Try to do so in a way that is not condemning of her father. See if I can enlist Lucy to support me on this issue(?)

Comment

This short exercise was very painful for Eve because she had to admit the intensity of the anger and the jealousy she felt toward Kristine, her former husband's new girlfriend. As Eve began to see how the anger and jealousy has made her act she was shocked because she realized that Kristine and Chuck's relationship was causing her to act in a manner she did not like. She didn't want them to affect her in this manner.

Eve also discovered that she had probably caused her two teenagers, Rosie, a fourteen-year-old, and Lucy, an eighteen-year-old, embarrassment and tension. She finally realized that all her anger and jealousy will not magically destroy Kristine, nor will it help Chuck and her to get back together. She decided to try to let go of this anger and jealousy and move ahead with her life.

Finally, Eve was upset that Chuck and Kristine's sexual relationship was causing her youngest daughter to question Eve's teachings about pre-marital sex. Eve realized that she had no desire to confront her former husband on his behavior, but she did want to make it clear to her daughter how she felt about sex before marriage. Eve hoped she might be able to recruit her oldest daughter to back her on this issue, but as she did the exercise she realized that she was not entirely sure that she would.

At the completion of the exercise, Eve was not sure of how to begin liking herself or dealing with her daughters about their father's sexual activity, but she knew that these tasks were where she wanted to put her energies. The emotions she felt doing this exercise were strong, but after she completed it she felt freer, more sure of herself, and happier than she had in a long time.

EXERCISES FOR AGES 12-14

If you are dating someone, plan an activity that includes your teenager. Be sure to pick a time convenient for your child and do an activity that he or she really likes: ball game, bowling, movie, etc. On this outing, make sure that you and your date include your teenager in all conversation.

A week or two later, select another activity for just you and your child. (If your budget is tight, just watching a T.V. movie together will do.) This will emphasize that while your son or daughter is welcome to develop a relationship with your new adult friend, you still enjoy spending time with just him or her.

Both of these activities can be repeated many times and with different adult friends of yours. Just be sure that you allow plenty of time for your adolescent to do things with his or her own friends, too.

EXERCISE FOR AGES 15-18

Tape the following list to your bathroom mirror and tie a pencil or pen to the sink. Leave it for your teenager to see:

"Guidelines" I would like Dad (or Mom) to follow when he (or she) dates:

1. _____
2. _____
3. _____
4. _____

Note: These are only "suggestions" to be considered, not "rules" to be followed.

If your adolescent responds, take the time to consider his or her suggestions. Decide what guidelines you can accept, including ones that perhaps your teenager did not even suggest. Then tape the following list on the mirror.

"Guidelines" I will follow when I date:

1. _____
2. _____
3. _____
4. _____

Note: These are only "guidelines," not "rules."

Later, share with your teenager why you agreed with certain ideas and not others—including those that just did not seem to be workable. Be willing to compromise if your teenager can suggest alternatives acceptable to you. In any case, let your child know you appreciate the suggestions and are sensitive to the problems that your dating might cause him or her.

If your teenager thinks this exercise is "dumb" and refuses to respond, do not get upset. Just let the matter drop. You have proved a willingness to open up a dialogue about your dating, and at a future time your son or daughter may feel free to bring up the topic again.

TABLE TOPICS

1. What are some of the differences between people dating at 16 and at 45?
2. Does anyone know a remarried family that seems to be happy? How do they accomplish it?
3. What does everyone think about the question of last names? Should women take their husband's last name? What name should the children have? What if there is a divorce? What if the woman then remarries?

CHAPTER 10

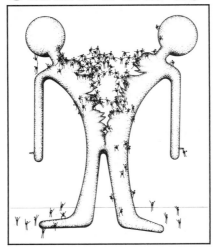

YOUR TEENAGER'S FUTURE

"I'm thinking about majoring in psychology when I go to college. I really know how it feels when parents get divorced and maybe I can help other kids."

Meredith, an eighteen-year-old

As teenagers finish their junior year in high school and throughout their senior year, ideas, worries, and plans about the future dominate their minds. (When they are not thinking about members of the opposite sex, that is.) Their thoughts revolve around the various adult roles and responsibilities that they will be facing in the not very distant future: worker, spouse, parent, friend, and citizen.

The divorce of their parents may or may not affect these concerns. Your adolescent's development has been influenced by many variables, such as genetic factors, state of health, family size, the community where you live, ethnic history, religious training, and special opportunities. Parental divorce is but an additional factor. If a teenager has come to understand and accept the divorce, there may be little negative effect on his or her development as an adult. If the divorce is recent, however, or has not been fully explored and accepted, it may well adversely affect your child's growth in one or more future adult roles.

Following her parents' surprise separation, Meredith began getting excruciating headaches. After a thorough physical exam had ruled out any physical reason for the illness, her mother, Veronica, made an appointment with her to see a counselor. Her mother hoped that Meredith would be more open with someone not personally involved in the family and that the headaches were only a symptom of the emotional stress brought about by the parents' troubles.

Meredith had always been an excellent student, but right after the divorce her grades dropped dramatically. She seemed to spend more time alone in her room, often just sleeping. She often didn't want to talk with either her mother or her father, Bert. Meredith was facing many emotional issues at the same time. It was her senior year in high school and she hadn't decided what to do after graduation. Her older brother had just gone away to college and she missed him. The house seemed empty without his noise and friends. Her father was also gone, and although he called her a couple of times a week Meredith felt uncomfortable at night with only herself and her mother in the house. In addition, Meredith had always been able to turn to her mother for support and encouragement, but now her mother seemed sad and preoccupied. This made Meredith feel even more alone, deserted, and frightened.

As Meredith talked with her counselor, she began to feel better and the headaches disappeared. Several times she asked her parents to attend a session with her. The family began to talk more openly about what was happening, and both parents were able to assure Meredith of their ongoing support. By the time her parents' divorce was final six months later, Meredith was doing better in school. Now Meredith was planning on going to the same college as her brother and majoring in psychology. Her parents' divorce had caused her pain, but from that experience she had developed an interest in helping children in similar pain. Thus, Meredith is incorporating her new awareness and concern into plans for her future roles as an adult.

WORKER

One primary adult role is that of worker. Being a member of the adult work force is a world that the adolescent will soon be facing. Most teenagers feel some dread at the prospect of accepting adult responsibility; they also long to be grown up, financially independent, and successful.

All healthy adult people are engaged in some form of work. Some people refer to their work as a career; this usually means that they have made an emotional commitment to their type of work, and in addition to time spent on the job they invest additional time and energy learning about and pursuing aspects of their career. In past decades it has usually been men who made a commitment to a career in addition to their family, although there have always been women who have pursued careers outside the home. Women who stay home to raise the children and create a family environment often make a "career commitment" to this role. People who have careers are certainly interested in the amount of money to be earned, but they also receive emotional satisfaction from their work.

Other adults view their work as a job or an occupation. They perform the tasks needed to be successful, but do not have an emotional commitment to it. If another job that pays more but uses completely different skills becomes available, they can easily switch jobs. People who view work in this way may go home feeling some anxiety or worry, but seldom invest emotional time and energy into work development. If they advance on the job—and many do—it is because they work very well. These people are often very skilled, careful workers, and get great satisfaction from doing quality work.

Jill and Karen are beauticians at a local hair salon. Jill views her work role as a career, and Karen sees it as a job. Jill attends national conferences where the latest hair styling and health trends are discussed, teaches two days a week at a vocational cosmetology school, and reads the hair styling magazines. In the future, she plans to open her own hair styling salon. Karen is a good hair stylist. She comes to work on time and is friendly with her customers. She is not committed to cosmetology, however. Karen has two other interests she would like to pursue: full-time homemaker/mother and nurse. Karen is not married, so her first interest is not yet attainable. To realize the second, she is currently saving money to go to nursing school. If Karen realizes either goal, she may then view her work as a career because she will feel emotionally committed to her work.

Virtually everyone works partially to make the money needed to survive and prosper. In this sense, all work is partially mere "toil." Most people, however, will experience their adult work as having some qualities of a job and some of a career. The critical dimension of any adult work is for the individual engaged in the work to feel satisfied and generally happy with what he or she is doing.

Your current attitude toward your work may influence your teenager's view of adult options. If you feel angry or cheated at having to work outside the home or feel trapped in a particular job because of child-support payments or child-care responsibility or even a need to live near your children, you may be communicating this to them. When a parent is unhappy with his or her work, the message communicated to the children is "adult work is miserable."

To help your adolescent develop a positive future, spend the time and energy in creating an adult work role for yourself that is as satisfying as possible. If your children view you as generally happy with your work, it will provide them with an adult model that says "adult work is satisfying."

Another way you can help your teenagers develop a positive attitude toward adult work is to expose them to the many different jobs people perform. You know your children's interests and abilities. Point out those types of work you think would use these attributes and discuss them from time to time. Arrange a time to discuss with your son's or daughter's school counselor ideas about future careers.

The final choice of adult work must be each person's, of course. Do not force a teenager into your mold, but rather encourage him or her to find the right path for himself or herself. All children need encouragement from their parents to explore many options.

From the time my son, Brian, was little, he loved to play school. As he went through high school, he would assess which teachers were good and why. He always loved going to school. When he went to college, however, he decided to major in pre-law because law was a career that guaranteed a good income. After graduation from college, Brian was accepted at an outstanding law school—and off he went to build a career that made lots of money. At the end of his first year of law school, Brian told me "Mom, I do not want to be a lawyer—I don't like law—I think I want to be a teacher." This made perfect sense to me. He was finally listening to himself.

In addition to my encouragement of Brian's interest in teaching, perhaps my contribution to his development has been being a person who loves her own adult work. He has seen me invested and interested in my career, with financial rewards being secondary to the personal satisfaction of being engaged in social work. Brian is now pursuing a path that uses both his abilities and his interests. I encouraged my son in his career, but the decision ultimately emerged from him.

Divorce can have another type of influence on the choice of adult work. If you were suddenly left with the need to have a job outside of the home, did not have the time or money necessary to develop your own career, or currently have a job that is not very satisfying but that you might have to keep "for the sake of the children," your child may vow never to be in that position. Rather than preparing for a homemaker role, your teenage daughter may insist on thoroughly preparing herself for a "meaningful" adult role that will provide her with income. If you have a teenage son, he may feel that before making a commitment to marry it is imperative for his prospective spouse to have a career outside the home that is satisfying to her. In other words, your divorce may result in your teen being very aware of—and perhaps even overly concerned with—the importance of being able to financially care for oneself and any dependent children.

Your divorce does not have to influence negatively your adolescents' response to adult work roles. It may, for example, encourage them to prepare carefully for self sufficiency; this certainly is not bad. On the other hand, it may cause them undue anxiety over financial security and self-doubt about their own abilities to function in the adult world of work. If both you and your children continue to work at accepting and understanding yourselves and the impact of the divorce on your lives, however, it will help you to have enough energy to support your career or job development and your teenagers to choose their own work interests.

SPOUSE

Being a husband or wife is another adult role that is in the foreseeable future for your adolescent children. They are forming attitudes and opinions on marriage now that will greatly affect their future actions.

It is normal and healthy to want to share your adult life with another person. To be able to take this step, one must be able to make an emotional commitment to that person. This commitment usually means you love, or deeply care for, your partner and are willing to share resources such as time, sex, money, and interests with him or her. It also implies sexual and emotional fidelity.

You were married; your marriage was a commitment to share your adult life with your former spouse. You promised to do so ". . . for better or worse, till death do you part." You now have experienced how a commitment made with affection and sincerity can change, shatter, and end. So have your teenagers. You may be somewhat bitter and disillusioned, perhaps feeling fearful about ever really trusting a commitment to another adult. So might they.

After a divorce it is very normal to feel hesitant and concerned about making another "lifelong" commitment to a new partner. For some, religious beliefs or laws make remarriage impossible while their former spouse is alive unless they receive an official annulment of their former marriage. Yet it is quite natural to long for and desire to share your life with a new someone. Before beginning any new relationships, however, please take the time you—and your teens—need to heal from the hurts and disappointments the ending of your marriage produced. During this time try to resolve and dissolve bitter feelings toward your partner. Continuing bitterness and anger will contaminate any new relationship and will sap the positive energies needed to invest in building a new life. If you cannot bring yourself to put the past behind you for your own good, do it for your children's future ability to have successful marriages of their own.

Your teenager witnessed the collapse of an adult commitment—the ending of his or her own parents' marriage. After parental divorce, adolescents often express doubts about ever marrying. The way you, as a parent, model your ongoing adult commitments may affect the type of partner to which your teen will make commitments in the future. You were a partner to your child's other parent, and that commitment ended. You have other commitments, however: to your parents, your children, your friends, your job. These commitments continue after the divorce. Has your son or daughter seen you keep your word, pay your bills, do special things for family and friends? Does your child see you respect and honor the divorce decree? If you meet another adult and make an emotional commitment to him or her, your teenager may draw ideas about commitments from observing that relationship.

These are tangible ways you can demonstrate to your children the ability to commit. As they reach adulthood, they will be able to use these positive experiences to help build their own adult relationships. Your divorce may result in your adolescent being somewhat cautious about marriage, but human beings usually want to have a close committed relationship. Thus, most children from divorced families will eventually marry. What you do now will contribute greatly to your teenager's ability to understand and fulfill that commitment.

Unlike the teen who decides he or she will never marry because of a parental divorce, some older adolescents may look to their girlfriend or boyfriend to soothe and comfort them in the period following the split in the family. As a parent, you may be worried that your child is getting "too close," spending too much time exclusively with this other teenager. You are rightly concerned that the young couple will make a premature commitment to each other—even marrying while still in their teens.

This concern is well-founded, since there is a higher rate of divorce for people who marry in their teens than in marriages between those in their mid-twenties. When parents try to "talk some sense" in this situation, however, or even break the couple up by forbidding contact, this may actually push the young people even closer together. Instead of overreacting, try to understand and accept your teenager's feelings. Continue to encourage future planning and patience. Realize you are entering a period in your adolescent's life during which there will be many things you cannot control. If the marriage happens, try to be as supportive as your can, but do not be surprised if things do not work out for the couple.

PARENT

In addition to having a satisfying work role and a successful marriage, most adults want to be parents. To parent, an adult should be able to nurture a needy, dependent baby and child. Good parenting requires one to be able to remember how it was to be a child, yet stay in the adult role of setting appropriate and safe boundaries. How you have parented will do more than anything else to make your own teenagers good parents when they grow up.

As you already know, parenting has many rewards, but it is also a lot of hard work. The relationship with your child is a lifelong commitment, stronger even than your marriage vows. Children truly are "non-divorceable." During the divorce process, the ability to parent is often strained. You may be experiencing considerable stress trying to adjust to the many changes and losses caused by your divorce and have little time and energy left to nurture your child. Unfortunately, just when parents are at this low ebb is when their teenagers—also suffering losses and changes—need them most.

Recognizing this need of your teens may help you be more available to them. Even when you are exhausted at the end of the day, for example, just watching a T.V. show or chatting about the day's events will be reassuring for both you and them. If your teenagers' grandparents or aunts and uncles live close by, perhaps they can supplement your parenting by occasionally taking them to a movie or the mall. Your local parish or congregation may also have a teen group that can serve as an additional outlet for your teenagers.

Becky's mother has been emotionally victimized by the divorce for several years. Her mother cannot discuss Becky's well-being or development with her father and continues to fluctuate between depression and rage. During the years since the divorce, her mother has fed, clothed, and schooled Becky, but she has not been able to emotionally parent—she has been unable to nurture.

This deprivation may have a harmful effect on Becky's own ability to nurture when she grows up and has children of her own. To be able to give to another person, especially to a little child, requires that a parent feel pretty good about himself or herself and have an inner source of empathy and giving that was built up by being emotionally cared for as a child. Becky is not getting this support from her mother, although her father, sister, grandparents, and teachers are supplying emotional nurturing. Only time will tell if it was enough for Becky to be able to be a nurturing parent herself.

Note: For some of you, unfortunately, you will have the experience of teaching your adolescent to parent when they themselves are parents. The statistics on teen pregnancy and parenting are too great to ignore this possibility. For the single parent or blended family, this can be one more unplanned complication. One thing to remember is that *your divorce is not the cause of your teenager's pregnancy.* Many teenagers whose parents are not divorced get pregnant. It is also important not to allow this development to stop your own parenting of your own child. Just because a teenager has a baby does not mean that he or she is an adult.

The most important thing you can do to help your teenager grow up with the ability to parent is to continue to put the energy and effort into parenting your own child.

FRIEND AND CITIZEN

Family and work roles usually make up the emotional center of one's life. There are, however, many other roles that adults are required to fulfill. Now, too, is the time when your adolescent children are forming their ideas about friendship and citizenship. Many of these roles can be very enriching, fulfilling, and supportive. In all of the events of daily life, you interact with others and are performing the role of friend, consumer, neighbor, volunteer, and citizen. It is in these roles that we go beyond our own narrow interests and concerns and exhibit the spirit of service, sharing, and giving.

Interaction with people outside the home and work help you feel connected to the community and the world. This type of connectedness helps people get through times of stress. People who have an established network of friends and acquaintances through community involvement usually adjust faster to divorce and other losses. Here again, it is up to you to provide the role model for your teenagers.

Ellen was devastated when her husband announced he wanted a divorce and left her with three adolescent children. For the past fifteen years Ellen and her former husband had lived in the same community. During those years, she had made many friends and acquaintances. The friendships were established through many different connections: work friends, friends made through years of active church membership, neighborhood friends, friends from her childhood, and friends from an exercise class. Although her divorce was very painful, Ellen had the help and support of many other people. She took an apartment in her old community, stayed a member of her church, even kept up her exercise class. She kept her friends, and they all supported her in her troubles. All of this communicated to her teenagers the nature of adult friendship.

Tom had always been interested in politics and for a time was involved in a local municipal campaign for the mayoral election. When he and his wife divorced, Tom experienced many lonely evenings—even though he had two teenage children. At the suggestion of a friend, he went to the local office of a major political party and began working as a volunteer for fifteen hours a month. It was the year of a presidential campaign, so there was a lot for Tom to do. In addition to having something to occupy his spare time, Tom met some interesting new friends, went to political rallies, and enjoyed making a contribution to a cause that was important to him. Tom's teenagers saw how this involvement was helpful to him and it taught them a valuable lesson about the benefits of civic involvement.

Tom and Ellen are examples of how people have used their connectedness and interests in the world outside of work and family to help them adjust to divorce. In both of these cases, the interests or friendships were established as a natural part of their adult life. By their own example, Ellen and Tom were helping their teens develop the skills necessary to live well-rounded adult lives.

Encourage your adolescents to be involved in activities and friendships. Allow overnights, chaperoned group parties, team sports, band or orchestra, and church-sponsored teen groups. Support their participation in programs that help others, such as walk-a-thons, food drives, and visiting the elderly. These experiences will give your teenagers exposure to outside institutions such as the church or synagogue and the "Y" or the public parks. From this exposure they will begin to view the world as a place where one can gain support and help others. Social interactions will help them develop the skills to make and keep friends and be involved in their community when they are adults.

A word of caution is in order: although you should allow your children to be engaged in activities outside of the home, do *not* push your teenager to get involved in outside activities. Some parents want their teenagers in some activity every afternoon of the week and on sports teams on the weekends. This is *too much* structured activity. Adolescents need plenty of time to just "hang out."

Your divorce does not need to hamper your teenagers' ability to have satisfying friendships and community involvement. As with all preparation needed for adult roles, their parents' ability to recover emotionally from the divorce is a most critical factor in teenagers' development. As you emotionally heal yourself, you will be able to support your adolescent children's participation in activities outside the home.

* * *

As a parent, you are entrusted with the care and nurturing of your teenager. The "end product" of all that activity should be an adult who has the ability to live independently, the skills necessary to raise a family, the spiritual and intellectual strength to function in society, and the capacity to care for and commit to others. In your role as a parent, you are supposed to eventually work yourself out of a job. Of course, you will love your children and be interested in them all your life, but your investment in "doing" for your teenagers should diminish as they do more and more for themselves.

EXERCISE 10
Imagining Your Teen's Future

FOR YOU

Write on a piece of paper these three columns: "How I Feel," "What I Am Communicating to My Teenagers," and "What I Can Do about It." In the center of the paper under these headings, write these four adult roles: "Worker," "Spouse," "Parent," and "Friend and Citizen." Under each category, list how your current attitudes and actions are affecting your teenagers' preparation for their adult roles. Decide which of your solutions you can initiate in the next week.

GERRY'S EXAMPLE

How I Feel	What I Am Communicating	What I Can Do
WORKER		
1. Bored	Being an accountant is a boring profession.	a. Ask my boss for a new assignment. b. Take some courses in new accounting methods.
2. Angry at not having the freedom to become a writer.	I don't have confidence in my own writing ability.	Send the short story I have been working on to a magazine.
SPOUSE		
1. Gun-shy. I make jokes about marriage.	a. Marriage is a very risky and difficult business. b. Being single is better.	a. Talk to my parents and others who have a good marriage. Take the children along. b. Read some good books on marriage.

152

PARENT

1. Upset at seeing the kids only every other week.	a. Maybe I don't enjoy seeing them.	a. Focus on how good it is when we are together.
	b. Their mother is to blame.	b. Ask my former spouse to allow some spontaneous dinners and visits.
2. Really pleased to be a father.	My children are loved.	Keep up the good work!

FRIEND AND CITIZEN

1. Sorry I've lost contact with my male friends.	a. You lose your friends when you get divorced.	a. Have a poker party with my friends while the kids are over.
	b. Friends aren't very important to men.	b. Talk to the kids about their friends.
2. Disgusted with politicians.	All politicians are crooked.	Take the kids with me when I vote.

Comment

Gerry, a divorced father who does not have custody of his three teenage children, did this exercise and realized how negative he was being with them. He decided that he really did not want to communicate this negativity to them and resolved to do things with them that would present a more positive image of the major adult roles.

On his work, Gerry resolved to do something to get out of his present situation. He realized that while he was not financially free to leave his accounting job, he could try to make his present job more interesting. He also resolved to pursue his interest in writing, even if it was only as a freelance writer.

Gerry felt very bitter about his divorce, and this was reflected in his attitude toward marriage. This exercise helped him realize that he was probably communicating this attitude to his teenagers.

Although he realized that he was communicating that he was upset with the current visitation arrangements, Gerry was certain that his children felt loved. He resolved to try to change the visitation agreement, but meanwhile he gave himself praise for his parenting. (It is important to recognize those things you are doing well!)

Finally, Gerry realized that he was losing contact with his male friends and that this was communicating the wrong message to his children—especially his sons. He also decided that his comments on politicians—even though they were done half in jest—might be forming negative attitudes in his children that he really did not want them to have.

EXERCISE FOR AGES 12-14

Cut out three pictures of what you think your teenager might look like or be doing in the future. Place these pictures on his or her bed or on the bathroom mirror with a note that says: "I've been thinking about your growing up and these pictures made me think of what you may be like in the future. Love, Dad (or Mom)."

See how your son or daughter reacts. He or she may ignore your message or think that you are weird, yet be secretly pleased you are thinking about his or her future. If your teenager wants to talk about the pictures, use this as an opportunity to begin to talk about the various adult roles to be faced. You might even ask him or her to cut out their own pictures of themselves in the future and leave them on your bed or bathroom mirror. This could turn into a fun "game" for the two of you.

EXERCISE FOR AGES 15-18

Take your teenager out for a grownup dinner (or lunch). If you have more than one child this age, take each one separately. Dress up as much as possible to emphasize the importance of the event, and encourage (but do not force) your son or daughter to do the same.

During the dinner, ask your adolescent about his or her hopes and visions for the future. What will be happening in five years? in ten? in twenty? Be prepared to be a good listener. Remember: no lectures about what *should* happen or even what *you* hope will happen. Be open to what your child is thinking. Based on what you hear, you may want to offer your opinions. Please wait until another time! Make this one occasion (at least) when your teenager knows for sure that you listened to what he or she was saying!

TABLE TOPICS

1. Should women return to work before their children are in school?
2. Is there such a thing as a "dead-end job"? If so, what are some examples?
3. What are the skills needed to be a good parent?

CONCLUSION

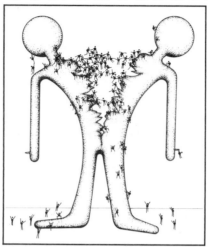

THE ONGOING NATURE OF DIVORCE

"I can't wait until this divorce is over."

Ellie, a twelve-year-old

"It will never be over."

Tim, Ellie's eighteen-year-old brother

Do not think that as you finish this book you are through helping your teenager deal with your divorce. The process will take a lifetime. Some people are still grappling with their parents' divorce when they themselves reach their forties.

Here are some final tips that may be useful to you and your teenage children in successfully navigating the process that takes you from the pre-divorce family to your current family and into the future.

1. Take care of yourself—physically, emotionally, and spiritually.

Every aspect of your children's well-being depends on you being healthy. When the shock of divorce first descends, you may feel very tired. Get the rest you need; go to bed earlier than usual, if necessary. Eat well-balanced meals, and do not overconsume alcohol or coffee. If your tiredness persists, see your doctor.

For your own emotional health, talk to others. You know how crucial it is to share your anger, worry, frustration, sadness, and successes with an understanding friend. Also, try to begin helping someone else; see if you too can

155

listen. Finally, listen to your inner self—your spirit. God's grace is always there when we need it. If you find your church or congregation a place where you sense peace and develop insights, continue to draw upon this support. The disillusionment of the divorce may have triggered a questioning of your former beliefs. If you reject them, both you and your children will be experiencing an additional loss—the loss of a spiritual base at a time when it is most needed.

All people need to sense a connectedness to their spirit, and this connectedness need not always mean formal religious activity. It has to do with an "inner knowing." There are many avenues to rebuild or to discover your spiritual dimension: talking with an understanding member of the clergy, walking in the quiet woods, playing the piano, reading, meditating, writing, and taking care of an infant or elderly person are examples of how some people have found their spiritual selves. By listening to your inner self you will discover a strength that can help you transcend this period of upheaval.

2. Let go of intense anger toward your former spouse (your child's other parent) for the hurt that he or she caused.

To help your children, the most important thing you can do—next to taking care of yourself—is to begin to dissipate the anger toward your former spouse for all of the wrongs that you feel were perpetrated against you. It may be difficult, or even impossible, to take this step, but even the effort is helpful. This does not mean you should never have felt anger toward your former spouse. It is very healthy to feel and express anger when someone has hurt you. If the anger remains intense, long after the hurtful incidents have occurred, however, it will definitely begin to interfere with your current, ongoing functioning.

Research that has explored how children adjusted after parental divorce find that those children who do best are those who have parents who maintain contact with them, parents who get on with their own lives, and parents who are not engaged in ongoing hostility. If you are not yet ready to give up your hate, then please try to set this as a future goal. If you do remain hateful, your children will suffer more than anyone else.

3. Try to build a co-parenting relationship with your former spouse.

The children who fare the best after parental divorce are those whose parents can discuss and share matters that pertain to them. This in no way implies that the divorced parents need to be best friends or chat about their own personal lives. It means that both spouses are entitled to know pertinent information about their children and participate in the important decisions affecting them.

Sharing report cards is a good start, but do not stop there. Share concerns about your teenager's future. Tell each other about your adolescent's dreams and concerns. Do not wait for the "other" parent to build this type of communication; take the initiative yourself.

Another word of caution: do not use the concept of "co-parenting" to try to get closer to your former spouse for romantic or other personal interests. This is using your children. A co-parenting relationship should be just what the term implies; two parents who care very much about their child, sharing ideas and tasks to help in successfully raising the child.

4. Provide and encourage alternative sources of support for your teen.

Adolescents need and deserve all the love, affection, and understanding that they can get. During the divorce process there may be many times when your energy and time will be consumed by the many tasks and emotions you are facing. If your teenager has additional sources of love and affection, he or she can draw upon these during the times you are feeling drained.

Grandparents can be a wonderful source of support. If they are the patient kind, grandparents will not mind driving their teenage grandchild to a shopping center to look for the perfect shoes or even allowing the adolescent to spend some time with them at their summer home. Let your parents—or your former spouse's parents—help support your teenager. Aunts, uncles, cousins, and adult friends are all additional possibilities for support for your adolescent. Pets are also a source of love and companionship. A family dog or cat does not talk back and will lay patiently watching your teen do homework or listen to the radio. Many teenagers say they feel less lonely when their pet is with them.

5. Encourage, but do not force, your teenager to express feelings.

There are teens who will not, or cannot, express their feelings. Some simply cannot label their feelings—they know they feel something but they don't know what to call it. Others do not want to tell anyone their feelings; they want to protect their private emotions. Still others may have repressed their feelings about the divorce to such an extent that they really believe that they have no feelings about it.

Of course, everyone involved in a divorce has some feelings about it. All children whose parents divorce have feelings about the divorce. If your adolescent refuses to share his or her feelings *do not* push, pry, or intrude; but do continue to be open yourself. Occasionally, share what you think your son or daughter, or any teenager, might be feeling in this situation, but allow your child the freedom not to comment.

Sometimes teenagers can be open about divorce feelings with someone other than their parents. This other person might be a close friend, a brother or sister, a teacher, or a counselor. Do not take it as a personal slight if your teen talks more easily to another about the divorce. Understand that if your adolescent does not share feelings with you it may be because he or she is trying to protect you or feels uncomfortable in sharing positive feelings about the other parent. Be happy that he or she can talk to someone; in time your child may be able to share with you.

6. Expect your teenager to have some feelings that are different from yours.

Adolescents are in the struggle of deciding who they are and who they will become. It is important for your teen to feel your continuing interest in him or her. Listen to his or her developing and changing ideas and opinions. Be willing to hear about happenings in peer relationships, drug use, school— even sex—that may be difficult to hear. Share your own feelings, but *do not lecture!* Instead, provide your son or daughter with feedback about her or his strengths and how these qualities will be useful in the future.

If your teen does share his or her feelings with you, it shows trust. Your son or daughter may think that your former spouse is very nice and express a desire to spend more time with that parent. If you have a bad look on your face when you hear these feelings expressed, or try to talk your teenager out of feeling a certain way, he or she will eventually get the message: "You can have feelings as long as they are exactly what I want you to have." When both parents send this message, children are put into a position in which they can never be honest. Try very hard not to convey this message; permit your adolescent to view the divorce from his or her own perspective.

7. Take the time and energy to parent.

Being a parent of an adolescent is seldom simple. It requires knowing your son or daughter well, encouraging the pursuit of dreams and goals, allowing freedom yet setting limits. Adolescents need encouragement to move forward in life, yet they don't have adult wisdom and experience. As a parent you need to know when to say "yes" and when to say "maybe, let me check" and when to say "no."

Single parents, especially mothers of adolescents, often have difficulty enforcing a "no." When a teenager can bully his or her parent on every issue, he or she becomes out of control. All children, adolescents included, need limits set. Many communities have parenting groups that teach these skills. If you are having problems setting limits, call your child's school counselor or the local mental health clinic to locate such a group in your area.

As difficult as it is for some parents to enforce a "no," for other parents it is just as difficult to say "yes." These parents see a world full of dangers and desire to keep their children safe by controlling every aspect of their lives.

158

This is, of course, impossible and undesirable! The more a parent *unreasonably* restricts a teenager, the more he or she will push away.

Thus, parenting a teenager is like walking a tightrope—one in which you cannot see the other end. Do not, however, let your divorce and your own needs get in the way. *Now* is when your teenager needs you more than ever, and this is the only chance you will have to parent him or her through the turbulent teens.

8. Be available to your teenager, but don't expect him or her to spend a lot of time with you.

During the process of divorce you may often feel overwhelmed with things to do. It may seem that there is little time left for your adolescent—especially since all they appear to want to do is to spend time with their friends. It is important, however, to try to include space for your teen. Let your son or daughter know that you will rent and watch a movie, proofread a paper for school, or be available just to talk. This type of attention will demonstrate to him or her that despite the divorce they are going to continue to be cared for. It will help your teenager feel secure—even if they seldom take you up on your offers.

9. Do things with people other than your teenager.

You are interested in your adolescent and are putting time and energy into helping him or her adjust to the divorce. This is necessary and commendable. But be careful not to let him or her become the only person or interest in your life. You need adult friends, too, and you need to spend some time doing adult activities, time without your teen. If you won't do this for yourself, do it as a role model for your soon-to-be adult child.

If you have other interests and friends, it will encourage your teen to have interests and friends outside the family. Your son or daughter will see you enjoying the outside world, and it will give him or her the message that it is possible to be a happy adult.

10. If either you or your teenager is having difficulties, consider seeking professional help.

Your divorce may be such a stressful process that—as hard as you may try to get your life functioning again—you may keep running into emotional, social, or financial problems. If you or your adolescent continues to feel intense bitterness, sadness, or helplessness, perhaps a professional counselor could be helpful. Social workers and psychologists that work with divorcing families often know of resources available in your community. Just becoming linked with the right support (money, legal, child care, job search, housing, health services, and so on) may lift a big load off your shoulders.

After all, neither you nor your son or daughter has ever gone through what you are going through now. How could you be expected to know what help is available? A professional counselor can also help you and your teen explore the troublesome aspects of your divorce. Many people feel more comfortable discussing very private feelings and events with a stranger who is a professional. The professional relationship is confidential and a counselor will be listening and thinking only of your well-being.

Perhaps you believe that you cannot afford professional help. Do not let that stop you! Some counselors charge on a sliding scale (the fees are fixed on the basis of your ability to pay), and many religious agencies and mental health agencies provide free counseling or will put you in contact with a counselor you can afford. If you feel that you would like to talk with such a professional counselor, get out your yellow pages and look under "Family Counseling," "Social Workers," or "Psychologists." Make a call or two to find out what is available.

Another alternative is to join a support group. There are a variety of such groups organized by churches or synagogues, schools, and social agencies. There are support groups for the recently divorced, for those without partners for whatever reasons, and for single parents. Such support groups allow you to share what you are going through with others who are experiencing or have been through the same things. You might find you even want to continue in such a group to help other people deal with the problems of divorce and single parenting.

Finally, use the exercises in this book whenever you think that they will be helpful to you or your teenager. Perhaps you may find some of them useful again in two or three years, when a younger child is a teenager or your younger teen is ready for the exercises for older teens or when your then young adult child expresses additional concerns or questions about the divorce.

* * *

Being a parent is a lifelong commitment that will bring you joy, anger, frustration, success, fun, worry, heartbreak, and satisfaction. The effort you have made to help your teenage children accept and understand your divorce is just one of the many, many responsibilities of parenthood. The fact that you are willing to make the special efforts involved in being a divorced parent is a large step toward fulfilling your commitment to your children—and to yourself.